Statistics 3

Edexcel AS and A-level Modular Mathematics

Greg Attwood
Alan Clegg
Gill Dyer
Jane Dyer

Contents

About this book

This book is designed to provide you with the best preparation possible for your Edexcel S3 unit examination:

- The LiveText CD-ROM in the back of the book contains even more resources to support you through the unit.

> Brief chapter overview and 'links' to underline the importance of mathematics: to the real world, to your study of further units and to your career

Finding your way around the book

> Detailed contents list shows which parts of the S3 specification are covered in each section

> Every few chapters, a review exercise helps you consolidate your learning

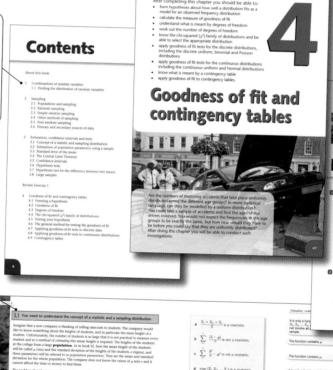

> Each section begins with a statement of what is covered in the section

> Concise learning points

> Step-by-step worked examples

> Past examination questions are marked 'E'

> Each section ends with an exercise – the questions are carefully graded so they increase in difficulty and gradually bring you up to standard

> Each chapter has a different colour scheme, to help you find the right chapter quickly

> Each chapter ends with a mixed exercise and a summary of key points.

> At the end of the book there is an examination-style paper.

LiveText software

The LiveText software gives you additional resources: Solutionbank and Exam café. Simply turn the pages of the electronic book to the page you need, and explore!

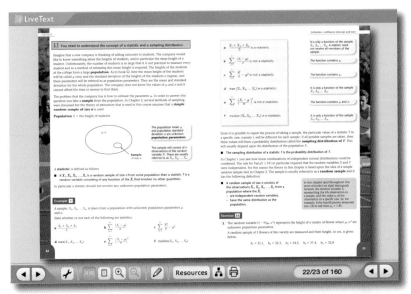

Unique Exam café feature:

- Relax and prepare – revision planner; hints and tips; common mistakes
- Refresh your memory – revision checklist; language of the examination; glossary
- Get the result! – fully worked examination-style paper

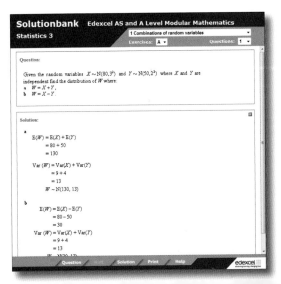

Solutionbank

- Hints and solutions to every question in the textbook
- Solutions and commentary for all review exercises and the practice examination paper

Published by Pearson Education Limited, a company incorporated in England and Wales, having its registered office at Edinburgh Gate, Harlow, Essex, CM20 2JE. Registered company number: 872828

Edexcel is a registered trademark of Edexcel Limited

Text © Greg Attwood, Alan Clegg, Gill Dyer, Jane Dyer 2009

14
10 9

British Library Cataloguing in Publication Data is available from the British Library on request.

ISBN 978 0 435519 14 8

Edited by Susan Gardner
Typeset by Tech-Set Ltd, Gateshead
Illustrated by Tech-Set Ltd, Gateshead
Index by Indexing Specialists (UK) Ltd
Cover design by Christopher Howson
Picture research by Chrissie Martin
Cover photo/illustration © Science Photo Library/Laguna Design
Printed in China (CTPS/09)

Acknowledgements
The author and publisher would like to thank the following individuals and organisations for permission to reproduce photographs:

Getty Images / PhotoDisc p1; Alamy Images / Kitt Cooper-Smith p7; Getty Images / PhotoDisc p21; Alamy Images / David Askham p67; Agripicture / Peter Dean p101.

Every effort has been made to contact copyright holders of material reproduced in this book. Any omissions will be rectified in subsequent printings if notice is given to the publishers.

Disclaimer
This Edexcel publication offers high-quality support for the delivery of Edexcel qualifications.
Edexcel endorsement does not mean that this material is essential to achieve any Edexcel qualification, nor does it mean that this is the only suitable material available to support any Edexcel qualification. No endorsed material will be used verbatim in setting any Edexcel examination/assessment and any resource lists produced by Edexcel shall include this and other appropriate texts.
Copies of official specifications for all Edexcel qualifications may be found on the Edexcel website – www.edexcel.com.

After completing this chapter you should be able to:

- combine independent normal random variables
- combine linear combinations of independent normal random variables.

Combinations of random variables

A sweet manufacturer produces two varieties of fruit sweet, Xtras and Yummies. The weights, X and Y, in grams, of randomly selected Xtras and Yummies are such that $X \sim N(30, 25)$ and $Y \sim N(32, 16)$. The manufacturer wishes to work out the probability that the average weight of a packet containing 6 Xtras and 4 Yummies lies between $28\,g$ and $33\,g$. By the end of this chapter you will know how to combine these distributions and work this out.

1.1 You need to be able to find the distribution of a combination of random variables.

■ If X and Y are two random variables then
  - $E(X + Y) = E(X) + E(Y)$
  - $E(X - Y) = E(X) - E(Y)$

■ If X and Y are two independent random variables then
  - $\text{Var}(X + Y) = \text{Var}(X) + \text{Var}(Y)$
  - $\text{Var}(X - Y) = \text{Var}(X) + \text{Var}(Y)$

The proofs of these relationships are not needed at this stage but they are used when combining independent variables.

Example **1**

If X is a random variable with $E(X) = \mu_1$ and $\text{Var}(X) = \sigma_1{}^2$ and Y is an independent random variable with $E(Y) = \mu_2$ and $\text{Var}(Y) = \sigma_2{}^2$ find the mean and variance of:

a $X + Y$, **b** $X - Y$.

a $\quad E(X + Y) = E(X) + E(Y)$	
$\qquad\qquad = \mu_1 + \mu_2$	
$\quad \text{Var}(X + Y) = \text{Var}(X) + \text{Var}(Y)$	
$\qquad\qquad = \sigma_1{}^2 + \sigma_2{}^2$	Variances are **always** added.
b $\quad E(X - Y) = E(X) - E(Y)$	
$\qquad\qquad = \mu_1 - \mu_2$	
$\quad \text{Var}(X - Y) = \text{Var}(X) + \text{Var}(Y)$	
$\qquad\qquad = \sigma_1{}^2 + \sigma_2{}^2$	

In S1, Chapter 8 the following properties of expectation were introduced.
- $E(aX) = aE(X)$
- $\text{Var}(aX) = a^2\text{Var}(X)$

■ Using these it can be shown that
  - $E(aX + bY) = aE(X) + bE(Y)$
  - $E(aX - bY) = aE(X) - bE(Y)$
  - $\text{Var}(aX + bY) = a^2\,\text{Var}(X) + b^2\,\text{Var}(Y)$
  - $\text{Var}(aX - bY) = a^2\,\text{Var}(X) + b^2\,\text{Var}(Y)$

  A linear combination of normal variables is also normal and so if $X \sim N(\mu_1, \sigma_1{}^2)$ and $Y \sim N(\mu_2, \sigma_2{}^2)$ and X and Y are independent.
  then
  - $aX + bY \sim N(a\mu_1 + b\mu_2, a^2\,\sigma_1{}^2 + b^2\,\sigma_2{}^2)$
  - $aX - bY \sim N(a\mu_1 - b\mu_2, a^2\,\sigma_1{}^2 + b^2\,\sigma_2{}^2)$

■ **The general form can be extended to any number of random variables.**

For example

$$X_1 + X_2 + \ldots + X_9 + Y_1 + Y_2 + \ldots + Y_5$$
$$\sim N(9\mu_1 + 5\mu_2, 9\sigma_1^2 + 5\sigma_2^2)$$

> $\text{Var}(X_1 + X_2) = \sigma_1^2 + \sigma_1^2 = 2\sigma_1^2$
> $\text{Var}(2X_1) = 4\sigma_1^2$
> $\text{Var}(X_1 + X_2) \neq \text{Var}(2X_1)$

Example 2

$X_1 \sim N(15, 3)$ and $X_2 \sim N(6, 2)$.
If X_1 and X_2 are independent find the distribution of Y where:

> $N(15, 3)$ means that the mean is 15 and the variance is 3.

a $Y = X_1 + X_2$,

b $Y = 4X_1 - 2X_2$.

> **a** $Y = X_1 + X_2 \sim N(15 + 6, 3 + 2)$
> $Y \sim N(21, 5)$
>
> **b** $Y = 4X_1 - 2X_2 \sim N(4 \times 15 - 2 \times 6, 16 \times 3 + 4 \times 2)$
> $Y \sim N(48, 56)$

> Using
> $X_1 + X_2 \sim N(\mu_1 + \mu_2, \sigma_1^2 + \sigma_2^2)$

> Using $4X_1 - 2X_2$
> $\sim N(4\mu_1 - 2\mu_2, 4^2\sigma_1^2 + 2^2\sigma_2^2)$

Example 3

If X_1, X_2 and X_3 are independent normal random variables such that $X_1 \sim N(8, 2^2)$, $X_2 \sim N(13, 2^2)$ and $X_3 \sim N(18, 3^2)$ and Y is a random variable defined by $Y = 3X_1 - X_2 + X_3$, find the distribution of Y.

> $Y \sim N(3 \times 8 - 13 + 18, 3^2 \times 4 + 4 + 9)$
> $Y \sim N(29, 49)$

Example 4

Bottles of mineral water are delivered to shops in crates containing 12 bottles each. The weights of bottles are normally distributed with mean weight 2 kg and standard deviation 0.05 kg. The weights of empty crates are normally distributed with mean 2.5 kg and standard deviation 0.3 kg.

a Assuming that all random variables are independent, find the probability that a full crate will weigh between 26 kg and 27 kg.

b Two bottles are selected at random from a crate. Find the probability that they differ in weight by more than 0.1 kg.

c Find the maximum weight, M, that a full crate should have on its label so that there is only a 1% chance that it will weigh more than M.

E

a Let $W = X_1 + X_2 + \ldots + X_{12} + C$

where $X \sim N(2, 0.05^2)$ and $C \sim N(2.5, 0.3^2)$:

$$E(W) = 12E(X) + E(C)$$
$$= (12 \times 2) + 2.5$$
$$= 26.5$$

$$Var(W) = 12\,Var(X) + Var(C)$$
$$= (12 \times 0.05^2) + (0.3^2)$$
$$= 0.12$$

$$W \sim N(26.5, 0.12)$$

$$P(26 < W < 27) = P\left(\frac{26 - 26.5}{\sqrt{0.12}} < Z < \frac{27 - 26.5}{\sqrt{0.12}}\right)$$
$$= P(-1.44 < Z < 1.44)$$
$$= (1.44) - (-1.44)$$
$$= 2(1.44) - 1$$
$$= 0.850\ (0.851)$$

> The weight of a full crate = the weight of 12 bottles plus the weight of a crate

> Using an extended version of $X_1 + X_2 \sim N(\mu_1 + \mu_2, \sigma_1{}^2 + \sigma_2{}^2)$

> Using $\frac{x - \mu}{\sigma}$

> Give your answer to a minimum of 3 s.f. You may use a calculator or the tables so both these answers are acceptable.

b $E(X_1 - X_2) = 0$

$$Var(X_1 - X_2) = Var(X_1) + Var(X_2)$$
$$= 0.05^2 + 0.05^2$$
$$= 0.005$$

$$P(|X_1 - X_2| > 0.1) = 2P(X_1 - X_2 > 0.1)$$
$$= 2P\left(Z > \frac{0 - 0.1}{\sqrt{0.005}}\right)$$
$$= 2(1 - (1.41))$$
$$= 0.159\ (0.157)$$

> The difference in weight between two bottles is required to be 0.1. Either bottle may be heavier therefore $X_1 - X_2 < -0.1$ or $X_1 - X_2 > 0.1$

> Give your answer to a minimum of 3 s.f.

c $P(W > M) = 0.01$

$$\frac{M - 26.5}{\sqrt{0.12}} = 2.3263$$

$$M = 27.3$$

> Look up 0.01 in the percentage points of the normal distribution table.

Exercise 1A

1 Given the random variables $X \sim N(80, 3^2)$ and $Y \sim N(50, 2^2)$ where X and Y are independent find the distribution of W where:

   a $W = X + Y$,   **b** $W = X - Y$.

2 Given the random variables $X \sim N(45, 6)$, $Y \sim N(54, 4)$ and $W \sim N(49, 8)$ where X, Y and W are independent, find the distribution of R where $R = X + Y + W$.

3 X_1 and X_2 are independent normal random variables. $X_1 \sim N(60, 25)$ and $X_2 \sim N(50, 16)$. Find the distribution of T where:

a $T = 3X_1$, **b** $T = 7X_2$, **c** $T = 3X_1 + 7X_2$, **d** $T = X_1 - 2X_2$.

4 Y_1, Y_2 and Y_3 are independent normal random variables. $Y_1 \sim N(8, 2)$, $Y_2 \sim N(12, 3)$ and $Y_3 \sim N(15, 4)$. Find the distribution of A where:

a $A = Y_1 + Y_2 + Y_3$, **b** $A = Y_3 - Y_1$, **c** $A = Y_1 - Y_2 + 3Y_3$,

d $A = 3Y_1 + 4Y_3$, **e** $A = 2Y_1 - Y_2 + Y_3$.

5 A, B and C are independent normal random variables. $A \sim N(50, 6)$, $B \sim N(60, 8)$ and $C \sim N(80, 10)$. Find:

a $P(A + B < 115)$, **b** $P(A + B + C > 198)$, **c** $P(B + C < 138)$,

d $P(2A + B - C < 70)$, **e** $P(A + 3B - C > 140)$, **f** $P(105 < (A + B) < 116)$.

6 Given the random variables $X \sim N(20, 5)$ and $Y \sim N(10, 4)$ where X and Y are independent, find

a $E(X - Y)$, **b** $Var(X - Y)$, **c** $P(13 < X - Y < 16)$. **E**

7 The random variable R is defined as $R = X + 4Y$ where $X \sim N(8, 2^2)$, $Y \sim N(14, 3^2)$ and X and Y are independent. Find

a $E(R)$, **b** $Var(R)$, **c** $P(R < 41)$.

The random variables Y_1, Y_2 and Y_3 are independent and each has the same distribution as Y. The random variable S is defined as

$$S = \sum_{i=1}^{3} Y_i - \tfrac{1}{2}X.$$

d Find $Var(S)$. **E**

8 A factory makes steel rods and steel tubes. The diameter of a steel rod is normally distributed with mean 3.55 cm and standard deviation 0.02 cm. The internal diameter of a steel tube is normally distributed with mean 3.60 cm and standard deviation 0.02 cm.

A rod and a tube are selected at random. Find the probability that the rod cannot pass through the tube. **E**

9 The weight of a randomly selected tin of jam is normally distributed with a mean weight of 1 kg and a standard deviation of 12 g. The tins are packed in boxes of 6 and the weight of the box is normally distributed with mean weight 250 g and standard deviation 10 g. Find the probability that a randomly chosen box of 6 tins will weigh less than 6.2 kg. **E**

10 The thickness of paperback books can be modelled as a normal random variable with mean 2.1 cm and variance 0.39 cm^2. The thickness of hardback books can be modelled as a normal random variable with mean 4.0 cm and variance 1.56 cm^2. A small bookshelf is 30 cm long.

a Find the probability that a random sample of

i 15 paperback books can be placed side-by-side on the bookshelf,

ii 5 hardback and 5 paperback books can be placed side-by-side on the bookshelf.

b Find the shortest length of bookshelf needed so that there is at least a 99% chance that it will hold a random sample of 15 paperback books. **E**

11 A sweet manufacturer produces two varieties of fruit sweet, Xtras and Yummies. The weights, X and Y in grams, of randomly selected Xtras and Yummies are such that

$$X \sim N(30, 25) \text{ and } Y \sim N(32, 16).$$

a Find the probability that the weight of two randomly selected Yummies will differ by more than 5 g.

One sweet of each variety is selected at random.

b Find the probability that the Yummy sweet weighs more than the Xtra.

A packet contains 6 Xtras and 4 Yummies.

c Find the probability that the average weight of the sweets in the packet lies between 28 g and 33 g.
E

12 If $X_1, X_2,..., X_n$, are independent random variables, each with mean μ and variance σ^2, and the random variable Z is defined as $Z = X_1 + X_2 + ... + X_n$, show that

$$\text{E}(Z) = n\mu \text{ and } \text{Var}(Z) = n\sigma^2.$$

A certain brand of biscuit is individually wrapped. The weight of a biscuit can be taken to be normally distributed with mean 75 g and standard deviation 5 g. The weight of an individual wrapping is normally distributed with mean 10 g and standard deviation 2 g. Six of these individually wrapped biscuits are then packed together. The weight of the packing material is a normal random variable with mean 40 g and standard deviation 3 g. Find, to 3 decimal places, the probability that the total weight of the packet lies between 535 g and 565 g.
E

Summary of key points

1 If X_1 and X_2 are independent random variables such that
$X_1 \sim N(\mu_1, \sigma_1^2)$ and $X_2 \sim N(\mu_2, \sigma_2^2)$ then
$X_1 + X_2 \sim N(\mu_1 + \mu_2, \sigma_1^2 + \sigma_2^2)$
$X_1 - X_2 \sim N(\mu_1 - \mu_2, \sigma_1^2 + \sigma_2^2)$

2 If X_1 and X_2 are defined as in 1 then
$aX_1 + bX_2 \sim N(a\mu_1 + b\mu_2, a^2 \sigma_1^2 + b^2 \sigma_2^2)$
$aX_1 - bX_2 \sim N(a\mu_1 - b\mu_2, a^2 \sigma_1^2 + b^2 \sigma_2^2)$

After completing this chapter you should be able to:

- take a simple random sample
- use random numbers for sampling
- take a stratified sample
- take a systematic sample
- take a quota sample
- know the circumstances in which each method of sampling might be used
- know the advantages and disadvantages of the different methods of sampling.

Sampling

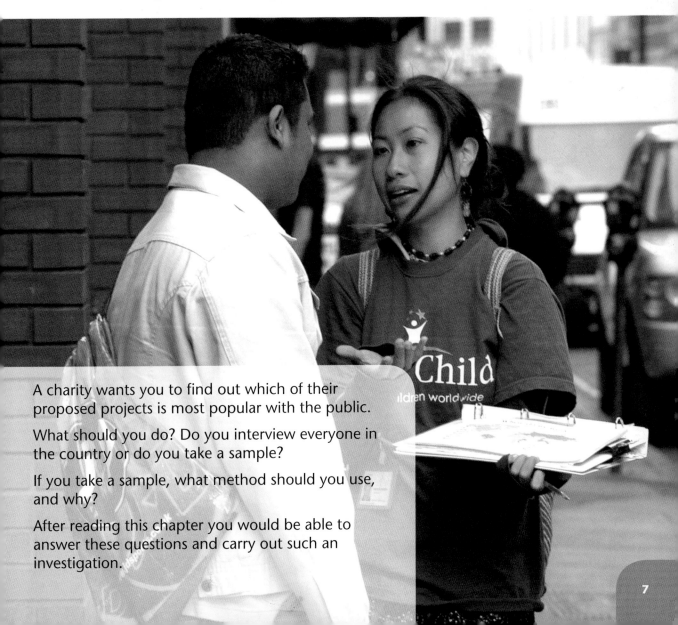

A charity wants you to find out which of their proposed projects is most popular with the public.

What should you do? Do you interview everyone in the country or do you take a sample?

If you take a sample, what method should you use, and why?

After reading this chapter you would be able to answer these questions and carry out such an investigation.

2.1 You need to know about populations and sampling.

■ Statistically a **population** is the whole set of items that are of interest.

> For example, if you wanted to find the mean height of students in a certain sixth form then the population would consist of the heights of all the sixth form students.

Information may be obtained from a population by taking a census or by taking a sample. The information obtained is known as **raw data.**

Taking a census

■ A census observes or measures every member of a population.

> To find the mean height of students in a certain sixth form, you could measure each student.

Perhaps the best known census is that conducted by the British Government. In this census every known householder in Great Britain receives a census form every 10 years. Each householder is required by law to complete and return the form by a certain date. The census form records a variety of information, such as the number of people present, their ages, and so on.

A census is used if

- the size of the population is small, or if
- extreme accuracy is required.

Sampling

■ A **sample** is a selection of observations taken from a sub-set of the population, which is used to find out information about the population as a whole. This is known as a **sample survey**.

> Suppose in a sixth form there were 400 students. Even though this number is quite small it would take a long time to conduct a census by measuring the height of each student. A sample of 50 would give you a good estimate of the mean of their heights.

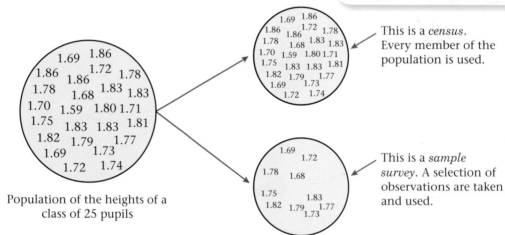

This is a *census*.
Every member of the population is used.

This is a *sample survey*. A selection of observations are taken and used.

Population of the heights of a class of 25 pupils

The sample will be truly representative of the population as a whole *provided that you select it so that it is free from bias*. To do this you must make sure that your selection is truly *random*.

The *size* of a sample (the number of people or units sampled) does not depend entirely on the size of the population. It depends on the *accuracy you require* and the *resources* you are willing to allocate to data collection. A large sample will usually be more accurate than a small one, but will need greater resources.

> The size of a sample will also depend on what you are going to use it for. Sample sizes as low as 10 or less have been used; while in a poll, where the population was all the people over 17 living in Great Britain, a random sample of 1500 adults aged 18+ was used.

The number of items or people sampled may also be affected by the *nature* of the population: if the population is very variable you will require a larger sample size than you would if the population were more uniform.

Both methods have advantages and disadvantages.

	Advantages	Disadvantages
Census	• It should give a completely accurate result.	• It is very time consuming and expensive. • It cannot be used when the testing process is to destruction (for example, testing an apple for sweetness). • The information is difficult to process because there is so much of it.
Sample survey	• A sample survey costs less than a census. • Results are obtained quicker for a sample survey than for a census. • Fewer people have to respond in the sample. • There is less data to deal with than in a census.	• The data may not be as accurate. • The sample may not be large enough to give information about small sub-groups of the population.

Example 1

Give a brief explanation, and an example of the use of,

a a census   **b** a sample survey.

> **a** Census – every member of the population is observed.
>
>   Example: 10-year national census.
>
> **b** Sample survey – a small portion of the population is observed.
>
>   Example: opinion polls.

Don't forget to give both an explanation and an example of use.

2.2 You need to know about random sampling.

In **random sampling** each unit is chosen entirely by chance and each member of the population has a known chance of being included in the sample.

Sampling with and without replacement

■ If the unit selected at each draw is replaced into the population before the next draw, then it can appear more than once in the sample. This is known as **sampling with replacement**.

■ If the unit is not replaced, so that only those units that have not previously been selected are eligible for the next draw, then it is known as **sampling without replacement**.

Two well-known examples of random sampling are ERNIE (Electronic Random Number Indicating Equipment), which is used to select winning numbers on Premium Bonds, and the selection of numbers for the national lottery.

2.3 You need to know about simple random sampling.

Suppose you wish to take a sample from a population of size N.

■ **A sample of size *n* is called a simple random sample if every other sample of size *n* has an equal chance of being selected.**

> We use capital N for the size of the population and n for the size of the sample.

Simple random sampling is sampling without replacement.

To do simple random sampling you need a sampling frame.

■ **A sampling frame is a list identifying every single sampling unit that could be included in the sample.**

Simple random sampling	
Advantages	**Disadvantages**
Provided that the population is small in size • it is cheap to do • it is simple to do • standard formulae can be used to analyse the results • each person or unit is included only once.	• It is not suitable where the population size is large. • A sampling frame is required.

There are two simple techniques that are commonly used and do not require elaborate equipment
• random number sampling
• lottery or ticket sampling.

Random number sampling

In **random number sampling** each element of the sampling frame is assigned a number.

> For a population of 400 you could assign the numbers 000, 001, 002, ..., 398, 399.

Once you have done this you can use tables of random sampling numbers such as the one at the back of this book (table on page 139). These tables contain 1000 or more digits, that is to say, integers starting from 0, i.e. 0, 1, 2, 3, 4, 5, 6, 7, 8, 9.

The table is constructed with great care so that each digit is equally likely to appear.

Suppose you want a sample of 50. You will need to select 50 random numbers from the table. You could start at the top left hand corner and work down the column. If you reach the bottom of the table you could start again at the top with the next unused digits along the top row.

> For a sample from a population of 400 you would need to take the digits in groups of 3, for example, 018, 276, etc.

To obtain a set of random numbers, you may start at the top of the table and read downwards, but it is better to start at a randomly selected place in the table, and you may travel in any direction. If a number appears that has already appeared, it is ignored (in effect this is then sampling without replacement).

Once you have extracted 50 random numbers, the sample is selected from the numbered sampling frame by using these numbers.

- In random number sampling, each element is given a number and the numbers of the required elements are selected by using random number tables or other random number generators.

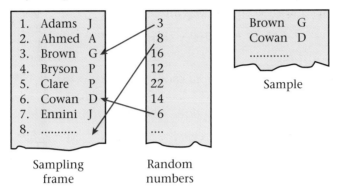

Sampling frame   Random numbers

Example 2

You are going to take a sample of 50 from a population of size 400. Write down the first five random numbers starting at the seventh column from the left of table on page 139 and working down.

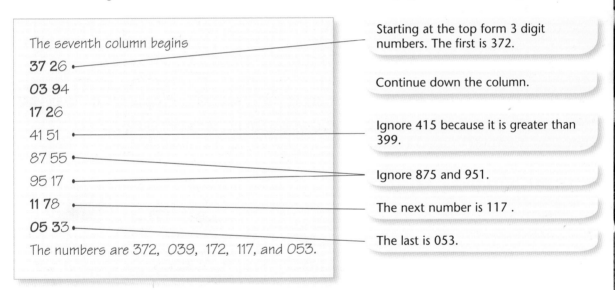

The seventh column begins

37 26

03 94

17 26

41 51

87 55

95 17

11 78

05 33

The numbers are 372, 039, 172, 117, and 053.

Starting at the top form 3 digit numbers. The first is 372.

Continue down the column.

Ignore 415 because it is greater than 399.

Ignore 875 and 951.

The next number is 117.

The last is 053.

Computers and calculators can produce lists of random numbers.

Random number sampling has advantages and one disadvantage.

Random number sampling	
Advantages	**Disadvantage**
• The numbers are truly random and free from bias. • It is easy to use. • Each number has a known equal chance of selection.	• It is not suitable where the population size is large.

Lottery sampling

In lottery sampling each element of the population is identified by some characteristic such as a name or number, and this is put on a ticket. The tickets, *which should all be the same size and shape*, are put into a container and are drawn one at a time (without replacement). The elements of the population corresponding to the tickets are selected.

Lottery sampling	
Advantages	Disadvantages
• The tickets are drawn at random. • It is easy to use. • Each ticket has a known chance of selection.	• It is not suitable where the population size is large. • A sampling frame is needed.

Example 3

Describe what is meant by a random sample, and give one advantage and one disadvantage associated with it.

A random sample is one in which every other possible sample of size n has an equal chance of being selected.

Advantage: It is free from bias. •——————————

Disadvantage: It is not suitable for large sample sizes.

Any of the other advantages could have been given here.

Example 4

The 100 members of a yacht club are listed numerically in the club's membership book. The committee wants to select a sample of 12 members to fill in a questionnaire about the facilities offered by the club.

a Explain how the committee could use a table of random numbers to take a simple random sample of the members.

b Give one advantage of this method over taking a census.

a Allocate a two-digit number to each person, starting at 00 and ending at 99.

Select a random starting point in the table. •——————

Select 12 random numbers. •——————

Go back to the original population and select the people corresponding to these numbers.

b A sample survey costs less than a census.

OR

Results are obtained quicker.

OR

Fewer people have to respond in the sample.

5th column and 7th row, for example
56, 86, 80, 57, 11, 78, 40, 23, 58, 40, 86, 14, 31 across.
56, 71, 66, 87, 09, 11, 48, 14, 33, 79, 12, 02 vertically.

Note you have to select 13 numbers in the first case because 86 occurs twice so is ignored the second time.

Exercise 2A

1 Explain briefly what is meant by the term sampling and give three advantages of taking a sample as opposed to a census.

2 Define what is meant by a census. By referring to specific examples, suggest two reasons why a census might be used.

3 A factory makes safety harnesses for climbers and has an order to supply 3000 harnesses. The buyer wishes to know that the load at which the harness breaks exceeds a certain figure.

Suggest a reason why a census would not be used for this purpose.

4 Explain:

   a why a sample might be preferred to a census,

   b what you understand by a sampling frame,

   c what effect the size of the population has on the size of the sampling frame,

   d what effect the variability of the population has on the size of the sampling frame.

5 Using the random numbers 4 and 3 to give you the column and line respectively in the random number table (table on page 139), select a sample of size 6 from the numbers:

   a 0–99   **b** 50–150   **c** 1–600

2.4 You need to know about other methods of sampling.

Systematic sampling

■ **In systematic sampling the required elements are chosen at regular intervals from an ordered list.**

To take a systematic sample, you take every kth element from a sampling frame, where k, the sampling interval, is calculated as:

$$k = \frac{\text{population size } (N)}{\text{sample size } (n)}.$$

For a sample size of 50 from 400

$$k = \frac{400}{50} = 8$$

Pick a number at random between 1 and 8, and if it is, say, the number 3, start at the third name on the list followed by the 11th, 19th, etc.

To overcome the objection that the first name is bound to be selected, you introduce a direct element of randomness by selecting the first item randomly.

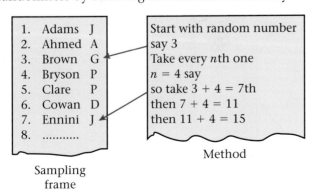

Sampling frame	Method
1. Adams J	Start with random number say 3
2. Ahmed A	Take every nth one
3. Brown G	$n = 4$ say
4. Bryson P	so take 3 + 4 = 7th
5. Clare P	then 7 + 4 = 11
6. Cowan D	then 11 + 4 = 15
7. Ennini J	
8. …………	

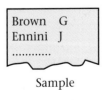

Brown G
Ennini J
…………

Sample

When you are selecting the interval, it is possible to introduce bias if you are not careful. Suppose you were investigating the mean rainfall each month over 100 years: an interval of 12 months would introduce bias, as you would be looking at the same month in each year.

Systematic sampling is used when:
- the population is too large for simple random number sampling.

Systematic sampling	
Advantages	**Disadvantages**
• It is simple to use. • It is suitable for large samples.	• It is only random if the ordered list is truly random. • It can introduce bias.

Stratified sampling

This is a form of random sampling in which the population is divided into groups or categories which are mutually exclusive, so no individual or item can be in two groups, and it is used where we may expect the observation of interest to vary between the different groups. These groups are called **strata** (singular: stratum). The strata would be decided according to one or more criteria such as gender, age, religion and so on.

For example, if the sixth form had 160 in the upper sixth and 240 in the lower sixth then the natural strata would be upper and lower sixth, and for a sample size of 50 we would take $\frac{50}{400} = \frac{1}{8}$ of each, that is, 20 upper and 30 lower sixth formers. In this way we can be sure of getting a balanced view with upper and lower sixth both proportionately represented, and with each student having an equal chance of being selected.

Within each of these strata a simple random sample is selected. The same proportion of each stratum is taken in the sample as is found in the population, so that each stratum will be represented in the correct proportion in the overall result.

$$\text{The number sampled in a stratum} = \frac{\text{number in stratum}}{\text{number in population}} \times \text{overall sample size}$$

- **In stratified sampling the population is divided into mutually exclusive strata and a random sample is taken from each.**

- **The proportion for each stratum is the same as that in the population.**

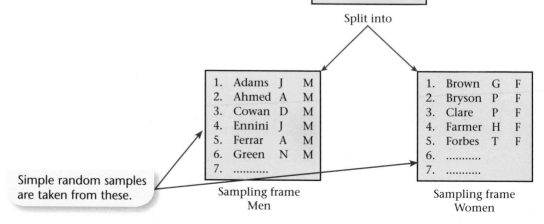

Sampling frame of population

1.	Adams	J	M
2.	Ahmed	A	M
3.	Brown	G	F
4.	Bryson	P	F
5.	Clare	P	F
6.	Cowan	D	M
7.	Ennini	J	M
8.	Farmer	H	F
9.	....		

Split into

Simple random samples are taken from these.

1.	Adams	J	M
2.	Ahmed	A	M
3.	Cowan	D	M
4.	Ennini	J	M
5.	Ferrar	A	M
6.	Green	N	M
7.	....		

Sampling frame
Men

1.	Brown	G	F
2.	Bryson	P	F
3.	Clare	P	F
4.	Farmer	H	F
5.	Forbes	T	F
6.	....		
7.	....		

Sampling frame
Women

Example 5

A factory manager wants to find out what his workers think about the factory canteen facilities.

He decides to give a questionnaire to a sample of 80 workers. It is thought that different age groups will have different opinions.

There are 75 workers between 18 and 32.

There are 140 workers between 33 and 47.

There are 85 workers between 48 and 62.

a Write down the name of the method of sampling the manager should use.

b Explain how he could use this method to select a sample of workers' opinions.

---

a Stratified sampling.

b There are: $75 + 140 + 85 = 300$ workers altogether.

Find the total number of workers.

In the 18−32 age-group;

he will select $\frac{75}{300} \times 80 = 20$ workers.

For each age group find the number of workers needed for the sample.

In the 33−47 age-group,

he will select $\frac{140}{300} \times 80 = 37\frac{1}{3} = 37$ workers

number = proportion of workers × 80

In the 48−62 age-group,

he will select $\frac{85}{300} \times 80 = 22\frac{2}{3} = 23$ workers.

Where the required number of workers is not a whole number round to nearest whole number.

The workers in each age group would be numbered and a random number table (or generator) would produce the required quantity of random numbers, the workers corresponding to these numbers would be asked their opinions.

Stratified sampling is used when:

- the sample is large and
- the population divides naturally into mutually exclusive groups.

Stratified sampling	
Advantages	**Disadvantages**
• It can give more accurate estimates than simple random sampling where there are clear strata present. • It reflects the population structure.	• Within the strata, the problems are the same as for any simple random sample. • If the strata are not clearly defined they may overlap.

2.5 You need to know about non-random sampling.

The chief characteristic of simple random, systematic and stratified sampling is that every individual has a known probability of being included in the sample − the sample is random. Non-random sampling methods are used when it is not possible to use random methods, for example, when no sampling frame is available. An example of non-random sampling is quota sampling.

Quota sampling

■ In quota sampling the population is divided into groups in terms of gender, social class, etc. The number of people in each group is set to try and reflect the group's proportion in the whole population. The interviewer selects the actual sampling units.

When taking a quota sample, as you meet people you assess their age or socio-economic group, etc. After they have been interviewed, they are put towards the quota into which they fit. This continues until all the quotas have been filled. If a person refuses to be interviewed, or the quota into which they would fit is full, then you simply ignore them and pass onto the next person. In practice you might also decide to take gender into account, but the more characteristics you introduce the harder it becomes to select people fitting all the characteristics.

For example suppose you wished to get an idea about how the people within your constituency are going to vote in an election. You would interview a different number from each age group.
You would then take a sample so that the proportions of each age represented the proportions present within the whole constituency.
The number beside each age group is known as the quota for that group.

A quota sampling scheme

Age group	Socio-economic group	Number/Quota
18−29	A/B	4
	C	13
	D/E	4
30−44	A/B	6
	C	17
	D/E	4
45−64	A/B	7
	C	17
	D/E	6
65−85	A/B	4
	C	12
	D/E	6
Total		100

Quota sampling	
Advantages	**Disadvantages**
• It enables the fieldwork to be done quickly because a representative sample can be achieved with a small sample size. • Costs are kept to a minimum. • Administering the test is easy.	• It is not possible to estimate the sampling errors. (The process is not a random process.) • The interviewer has to choose the respondents and may not be able to judge the characteristics easily. • Non-responses are not recorded. (Perhaps the non-respondent in the constituency survey did not agree to be interviewed because he was a 'don't know' voter.) • It can introduce interviewer bias in who is included.

2.6 You need to know about primary and secondary sources of data.

■ **Primary data** are data that is collected by, or on behalf of, the person who is going to use the data.

■ **Secondary data** are data that is neither collected by, nor on behalf of, the person who is to use the data. The data are second hand.

Type of data	Advantages	Disadvantages
Primary data	• The collection method is known. • The accuracy is known. • The exact data needed are collected.	• It is costly in time and effort.
Secondary data	• They are cheap to obtain – government publications, for example, are relatively cheap. • A large quantity of data is available, for example, on the internet. • Much of the data has been collected for years and can be used to plot trends.	• Bias is not always recognised. • It can be in a form that is difficult to deal with.

Exercise 2B

1 Explain briefly the difference between a census and a sample survey.
  Write brief notes on:

  a simple random sampling,
  b stratified sampling,
  c systematic sampling,
  d quota sampling.

  Your notes should include the definition, and any advantages and disadvantages associated with each method of sampling.

2 **a** Explain the purpose of stratification in carrying out a sample survey.

  b The headteacher of an infant school wishes to take a stratified sample of 20% of the pupils at his school. The school has the following numbers of pupils.

Year 1	Year 2	Year 3
40	60	80

  Work out how many pupils in each age group there will be in the sample.

3 A survey is to be done on the adult population of a certain city suburb, the population of which is 2000. An ordered list of the inhabitants is available.

  a What sampling method would you use and why?

  b What condition would have to be applied to your ordered list if the selection is to be truly random?

4 In a marketing sample survey the sales of cigarettes in a variety of outlets is to be investigated. The outlets consist of small kiosks selling cigarettes and tobacco only, tobacconist's shops that sell cigarettes and related products and shops that sell cigarettes and other unrelated products.

   a Suggest the most suitable form of taking a random sample.

   b Explain how you would conduct the sample survey.

   c What are the advantages and disadvantages of the method chosen?

5 **a** Explain briefly:

      i why it is often desirable to take samples,

      ii what you understand by a sampling frame.

   b State one circumstance when you would consider using

      i systematic sampling,

      ii stratification when sampling from a population,

      iii quota sampling.

6 A factory manager wants to get information about the ways his workers travel to work. There are 480 workers in the factory, and each has a clocking in number. The numbers go from 1 to 480. Explain how the manager could take a systematic sample of size 30 from these workers.

Mixed exercise 2C

1 Using the random numbers on page 139, and starting at the top of the column with the number 88 and working down, a simple random sample (without replacement) of size 10 was taken of numbers between 0 and 75 inclusive. The first two numbers were 17 and 52.

   a Find the other eight numbers in the sample.

   b Explain, with the aid of a practical situation, how this set of random numbers could be used to take a sample of size 10.   **E**

2 **a** Give one advantage and one disadvantage of using

      i a census,   **ii** a sample survey.

   b It is decided to take a sample of 100 from a population consisting of 500 elements. Explain how you would obtain a simple random sample without replacement from this population.   **E**

3 **a** Explain briefly what you understand by

      i a population,

      ii a sampling frame.

   b A market research organisation wants to take a sample of

      i owners of diesel motor cars in the UK,

      ii persons living in Oxford who suffered from injuries to the back during July 1996.

      Suggest a suitable sampling frame in each case.   **E**

4 A gym keeps a numbered alphabetical list of their 200 clients.

   Explain how you would choose a simple random sample of 40 clients.

5 Write down one advantage and one disadvantage of using:

   a stratified sampling,   **b** simple random sampling.

6 The managing director of a factory wants to know what the workers think about the factory canteen facilities. One hundred people work in the offices and 200 work on the shop floor.

He decides to ask the people who work in the offices.

a Suggest reasons why this is likely to produce a biased sample.

b Explain briefly how the factory manager could select a sample of 30 workers using:

    i systematic sampling,

    ii stratified sampling,

    iii quota sampling.

7 A garden centre employs 150 workers. Sixty-five of the workers are women and 85 are men. Explain briefly how you would take a random sample of 30 workers using stratified sampling.

8 The 240 members of a bowling club are listed alphabetically in the club's membership book. The committee wishes to select a sample of 30 members to fill in a questionnaire about the facilities the club has to offer.

a Explain how the committee could use a table of random numbers to take a systematic sample.

b Give one advantage of this method over taking a simple random sample. *E*

9 a Explain briefly what you understand by:

    i a population,   **ii** a sample.

b Give one advantage and one disadvantage of taking a sample.

10 A college of 3000 students has students registered in four departments: arts, science, education and crafts. The principal wishes to take a sample from the student population to gain information about the likely student response to a rearrangement of the college timetable in order to hold lectures on Wednesday, previously reserved for sports.

What sampling method would you advise the principal to use? Give reasons to justify your choice. *E*

11 As part of her statistics project, Deepa decided to estimate the amount of time A-level students at her school spent on private study each week. She took a random sample of students from those studying arts subjects, science subjects and a mixture of arts and science subjects. Each student kept a record of the time they spent on private study during the third week of term.

a Write down the name of the sampling method used by Deepa.

b Give a reason for using this method and give one advantage this method has over simple random sampling. *E*

12 There are 64 girls and 56 boys in a school.

Explain briefly how you could take a random sample of 15 pupils using

a a simple random sample,

b a stratified sample. *E*

Summary of key points

1   A **population** is the whole set of items that are of interest.

2   A **census** observes or measures every member of a population.

3   A sample is a selection of observations taken from a sub-set of the population which is used to find out information about the population as a whole. This is known as a **sample survey**.

4   A **random sample** is one in which every possible sample of size n has an equal chance of being selected.

5   A **sampling frame** is a list identifying every single sampling unit that could be included in the sample.

6   In random number sampling, each element is given a number to identify it and the numbers of the required elements are selected by using random number tables or other random number generators.

7   In systematic sampling the required elements are chosen at regular intervals from an ordered list.

8   In stratified sampling the population is divided into mutually exclusive strata and a simple random sample is taken from each. The proportion of the strata in the sample is the same as the proportion of the strata in the population.

9   In quota sampling the population is divided into groups in terms of gender, social class, etc. The number of people in each group is set to try and reflect the group's proportion in the whole population. The interviewer selects the actual sampling units.

After studying this chapter you should

- understand the concept of an unbiased estimate
- appreciate the significance of the Central Limit Theorem
- know how to find confidence intervals for the population mean μ
- be able to test hypotheses about the population mean μ.

Estimation, confidence intervals and tests

The doctors say Jim is of average height. In fact, he is 1.84 m tall; but how can you find the average height of adult men? John was also told that he was of average height, but he is 1.88 m tall. Does this mean that the doctors are using a range of values to describe average height, say 1.80 to 1.90 m perhaps? Paul is 1.92 m tall but he claims to be of average height. How can you test this claim, and what basis could you give for saying that Paul was above average height? In this chapter you will examine ways of finding estimates, as well as using probability to test claims like Paul's.

3.1 You need to understand the concept of a statistic and a sampling distribution

Imagine that a new company is thinking of selling raincoats to students. The company would like to know something about the heights of students, and in particular the *mean* height of a student. Unfortunately, the number of students is so large that it is not practical to measure every student and so a method of *estimating* this mean height is required. The heights of the students at the college form a large **population**. As in book S2, here the mean height of the students will be called μ (mu) and the standard deviation of the heights of the students σ (sigma), and these parameters will be referred to as population parameters. They are the mean and standard deviation for the whole population. The company does not know the values of μ and σ and it cannot afford the time or money to find them.

The problem that the company has is how to *estimate* the parameter μ. In order to answer this question you take a **sample** from the population. In Chapter 2, several methods of sampling were discussed but the theory of estimation that is used in this course assumes that a **simple random sample of size n** is used.

Population X = the height of students

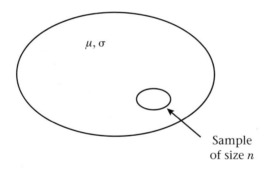

The population mean μ and population standard deviation σ are unknown **population parameters**.

Sample of size n

The sample will consist of n observations of the random variable X. These are usually referred to as $X_1, X_2, ..., X_n$.

A **statistic** is defined as follows

■ **If $X_1, X_2, X_3, ..., X_n$ is a random sample of size n from some population then a statistic T is a random variable consisting of any function of the X_i that involves no other quantities.**

In particular a statistic should not involve any unknown population parameters.

Example 1

A sample, $X_1, X_2, ..., X_n$, is taken from a population with unknown population parameters μ and σ.

State whether or not each of the following are statistics.

a $\dfrac{X_1 + X_3 + X_5}{3}$

b $\displaystyle\sum_{i=1}^{n} \dfrac{|X_i - \mu|}{n}$

c $\displaystyle\sum_{i=1}^{n} \dfrac{X_i^2}{n} - \mu^2$

d $\max(X_1, X_2, ..., X_n)$

e $\displaystyle\sum_{i=1}^{n} \left(\dfrac{X_i - \mu}{\sigma}\right)^2$

f $\text{median}(X_1, X_2, ..., X_n)$

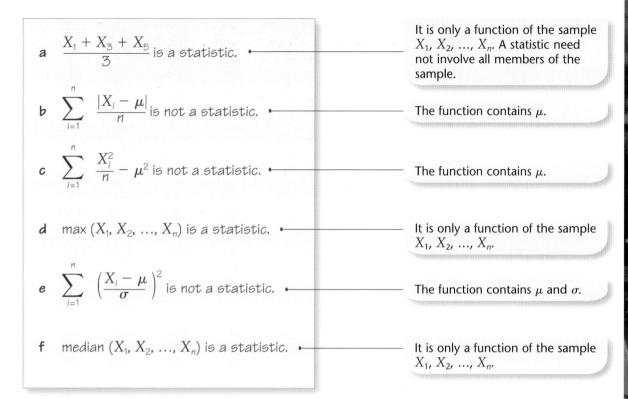

a $\dfrac{X_1 + X_3 + X_5}{3}$ is a statistic. — It is only a function of the sample $X_1, X_2, \ldots, X_n$. A statistic need not involve all members of the sample.

b $\displaystyle\sum_{i=1}^{n} \dfrac{|X_i - \mu|}{n}$ is not a statistic. — The function contains μ.

c $\displaystyle\sum_{i=1}^{n} \dfrac{X_i^2}{n} - \mu^2$ is not a statistic. — The function contains μ.

d $\max(X_1, X_2, \ldots, X_n)$ is a statistic. — It is only a function of the sample $X_1, X_2, \ldots, X_n$.

e $\displaystyle\sum_{i=1}^{n} \left(\dfrac{X_i - \mu}{\sigma}\right)^2$ is not a statistic. — The function contains μ and σ.

f $\text{median}(X_1, X_2, \ldots, X_n)$ is a statistic. — It is only a function of the sample $X_1, X_2, \ldots, X_n$.

Since it is possible to repeat the process of taking a sample, the particular value of a statistic T in a specific case, namely t, will be different for each sample. If all possible samples are taken, then these values will form a probability distribution called the **sampling distribution of T**. This will usually depend upon the distribution of the population X.

■ **The sampling distribution of a statistic T is the probability distribution of T.**

In Chapter 1 you saw how linear combinations of independent normal distributions could be combined. The rule for $\text{Var}(aX \pm bY)$ in particular required that the random variables X and Y were independent. For this reason the theory in this chapter is based upon the idea of a simple random sample met in Chapter 2. The sample is usually referred to as a **random sample** and it has the following definition:

■ **A random sample of size n consists of the observations $X_1, X_2, X_3, \ldots, X_n$ from a population where the X_i**
  ○ **are independent random variables,**
  ○ **have the same distribution as the population.**

In this chapter (and throughout this series of books) we shall distinguish between the random variable X_i representing the ith observation in a sample, and the value x_i of the observation in a *specific case*. So, for example, if the fourth person measured was 1.85 m tall then $x_4 = 1.85$.

Example 2

The noon day temperature, in °C, is measured for a random sample of 5 days in July in a certain city and the following results were obtained

$$28.3, \quad 31.2, \quad 24.0, \quad 28.7, \quad 30.9$$

Calculate the values of the following statistics

a $\bar{X}$ **b** $\sum X_i^2$ **c** $\max(X_1, X_2, \ldots, X_n) - \min(X_1, X_2, \ldots, X_n)$

a $\bar{x} = \dfrac{\sum x}{n} = \dfrac{28.3 + 31.2 + \ldots + 30.9}{5}$

$= \dfrac{143.1}{5} = 28.62$

> We use $\bar{x}$ for the mean value and $\overline{X}$ for the mean of the statistic.

b $\sum X_i^2 = 28.3^2 + 31.2^2 + \ldots + 30.9^2$

$= 4128.83$

c The minimum value is 24.0
The maximum value is 31.2
The statistic has a value of $31.2 - 24.0 = 7.2$

> This, of course, is the statistic commonly known as the range.

If the distribution of the population is known then the sampling distribution of a statistic can sometimes be found.

Example 3

The weights, in grams, of a consignment of apples are normally distributed with a mean μ and standard deviation 4. A sample of size 25 is taken and the statistics R and T are calculated as follows:

$$R = X_{25} - X_1 \text{ and } T = X_1 + X_2 + \ldots + X_{25}$$

Find the distributions of R and T.

The sample will be $X_1, X_2, \ldots, X_{25}$ where each $X_i \sim N(\mu, 4^2)$.	State the distribution for each of the X_i.
Now: $\qquad R = X_{25} - X_1 \Rightarrow R \sim N(\mu - \mu, 4^2 + 4^2)$	
that is: $\qquad R \sim N\left(0, [4\sqrt{2}]^2\right)$	Use the formulae for $E(X - Y)$ and $\text{Var}(X - Y)$ from Chapter 1.
Also $\qquad T = X_1 + X_2 + \ldots + X_{25}$	
so: $\qquad T \sim N(25\mu, 25 \times 4^2)$	Extend the formulae for $E(X + Y)$ and $\text{Var}(X - Y)$ from Chapter 1.
or $\qquad T \sim N(25\mu, 20^2)$	

Example 4

A large bag contains counters. Sixty per cent of the counters have the number 0 on them and forty per cent have the number 1.

a Find the mean μ and variance σ^2 for this population of counters.

A simple random sample of size 3 is taken from this population.

b List all possible samples.

c Find the sampling distribution for the mean

$$\overline{X} = \dfrac{X_1 + X_2 + X_3}{3}$$

where X_1, X_2 and X_3 are the three variables representing samples 1, 2 and 3.

d Hence find $E(\overline{X})$ and $\text{Var}(\overline{X})$.

e Find the sampling distribution for the mode M.

f Hence find $E(M)$ and $\text{Var}(M)$.

a The distribution of the population is

$$x: \qquad 0 \qquad 1$$
$$P(X = x): \qquad \frac{3}{5} \qquad \frac{2}{5}$$

> Use the methods from S1 to find μ and σ.

$$\mu = E(X) = \sum_{\forall x} xP(X = x) = 0 + \frac{2}{5} \Rightarrow \mu = \frac{2}{5}$$

$$\sigma^2 = Var(X) = \sum_{\forall x} x^2 P(X = x) - \mu^2 = 0 + 1^2 \times \frac{2}{5} - \frac{4}{5} \Rightarrow \sigma^2 = \frac{6}{25}$$

b The possible samples are

$$(0, 0, 0)$$
$$(1, 0, 0) \ (0, 1, 0) \ (0, 0, 1)$$
$$(1, 1, 0) \ (1, 0, 1) \ (0, 1, 1)$$
$$(1, 1, 1)$$

> List these systematically.

> Since the sample is random the observations are independent. So to find the probability of case (1, 0, 0) you can multiply the probabilities $P(X_1 = 1) \times P(X_2 = 0) \times P(X_3 = 0)$ Remember that each X_i has the same distribution as X.

c $P(\overline{X} = 0) = \left(\frac{3}{5}\right)^3 = \frac{27}{125}$ i.e. the $(0, 0, 0)$ case

$P(\overline{X} = \frac{1}{3}) = 3 \times \frac{2}{5} \times \left(\frac{3}{5}\right)^2 = \frac{54}{125}$ i.e. the $(1, 0, 0)$; $(0, 1, 0)$; $(0, 0, 1)$ cases

$P(\overline{X} = \frac{2}{3}) = 3 \times \left(\frac{2}{5}\right)^2 \times \frac{3}{5} = \frac{36}{125}$ i.e. the $(1, 1, 0)$; $(1, 0, 1)$; $(0, 1, 1)$ cases

$P(\overline{X} = 1) = \left(\frac{2}{5}\right)^3 = \frac{8}{125}$ i.e. the $(1, 1, 1)$ case.

So the distribution for $\overline{X}$ is

$\overline{X}:$	0	$\frac{1}{3}$	$\frac{2}{3}$	1
$p(\overline{x}):$	$\frac{27}{125}$	$\frac{54}{125}$	$\frac{36}{125}$	$\frac{8}{125}$

> General formulae for $E(\overline{X})$ and $Var(\overline{X})$ are given in Section 3.2.

d $E(\overline{X}) = 0 + \frac{1}{3} \times \frac{54}{125} + \frac{2}{3} \times \frac{36}{125} + 1 \times \frac{8}{125} = \frac{18 + 24 + 8}{125} = \frac{2}{5}$

$Var(\overline{X}) = 0 + \frac{1}{9} \times \frac{54}{125} + \frac{4}{9} \times \frac{36}{125} + 1 \times \frac{8}{125} - \frac{4}{25} = \frac{6 + 16 + 8}{125} - \frac{20}{125} = \frac{2}{25}$

e The mode M can take values 0 or 1.

$$P(M = 0) = \frac{27}{125} + \frac{54}{125} = \frac{81}{125} \qquad [\text{i.e. cases } (0, 0, 0); (1, 0, 0); (0, 1, 0); (0, 0, 1)]$$

and $P(M = 1) = \frac{44}{125}$ $[\text{i.e. the other cases}]$

so the distribution of M is

$M:$	0	1
$p(m):$	$\frac{81}{125}$	$\frac{44}{125}$

f $$E(M) = 0 + 1 \times \frac{44}{125} = \frac{44}{125}$$

and $$Var(M) = 0 + 1 \times \frac{44}{125} - \left(\frac{44}{125}\right)^2 = 0.228$$

Notice that $E(\overline{X}) = \mu$ but $E(M) \neq \mu$ and that neither $E(\overline{X})$ nor $E(M)$ are equal to the population mode, which is of course zero as 60% of the counters have a zero on them. These results will be examined in greater detail in Section 3.2.

Exercise 3A

1 The random variable $H \sim N(\mu, \sigma^2)$ represents the height of a variety of flower where μ, σ^2 are unknown population parameters.

A random sample of 5 flowers of this variety are measured and their height, in cm, is given below.

$$h_1 = 35.1, \quad h_2 = 32.3, \quad h_3 = 34.5, \quad h_4 = 37.4, \quad h_5 = 32.8$$

Determine which of the following are statistics.

a $\displaystyle\sum_{i=1}^{5} (X_i - \mu)$

b $\displaystyle\sum_{i=1}^{5} \frac{(X_i - \bar{X})^2}{4}$

c $\displaystyle\sum \left| \frac{X_i - \mu}{\sigma} \right|$

d $X_1 - X_5$

2 A random sample of 6 apples are weighed and their weights, x_i g, are recorded

$$x_1 = 168, \quad x_2 = 185, \quad x_3 = 161, \quad x_4 = 172, \quad x_5 = 187, \quad x_6 = 176$$

Calculate the values of the following statistics.

a $\displaystyle\frac{X_6 + X_1}{2}$

b $\displaystyle\sum_{i=1}^{6} \frac{(X_i - \bar{X})^2}{6}$

c $\displaystyle\frac{\sum_{i=1}^{6} X_i^2}{\sum_{i=1}^{6} X_i}$

3 The lengths of nails produced by a certain machine are normally distributed with a mean μ and standard deviation σ. A random sample of 10 nails is taken and their lengths $\{X_1, X_2, X_3, ..., X_{10}\}$ are measured.

i Write down the distributions of the following:

a $\displaystyle\sum_{1}^{10} X_i$

b $\displaystyle\frac{2X_1 + 3X_{10}}{5}$

c $\displaystyle\sum_{1}^{10} (X_i - \mu)$

d $\bar{X}$

e $\displaystyle\sum_{1}^{5} X_i - \sum_{6}^{10} X_i$

f $\displaystyle\sum_{1}^{10} \left(\frac{X_i - \mu}{\sigma} \right)$

ii State which of the above are statistics.

4 A large bag of coins contains 1p, 5p and 10p coins in the ratio 2:2:1.

a Find the mean μ and the variance σ^2 for the value of coins in this population.

A random sample of two coins is taken and their values X_1 and X_2 are recorded.

b List all possible samples.

c Find the sampling distribution for the mean $\bar{X} = \dfrac{X_1 + X_2}{2}$.

d Hence show that $E(\bar{X}) = \mu$ and $Var(\bar{X}) = \dfrac{\sigma^2}{2}$.

3.2 You need to be able to estimate population parameters using a sample.

In Section 3.1, the problem of trying to estimate the mean height of students in a sixth form college was considered. If you take a random sample of size n then you can find various statistics. The question is, are any of these statistics useful in estimating the population parameters?

A statistic that is used to estimate a population parameter is called an **estimator**: the particular value of this estimator generated by a particular sample is called an **estimate**.

Since all the X_i are random variables having the same mean and variance as the population, you can sometimes find expected values of a statistic T, E(T), and this will tell you what the 'average' value of the statistic should be.

Example 5

A random sample X_1, X_2, ..., X_n is taken from a population with $X \sim N(\mu, \sigma^2)$.
Show that $E(\overline{X}) = \mu$.

In Chapter 8 of book S1 an important property of expected values was given:

$E(aX) = aE(X)$ ①

Also in Chapter 1 of this book you saw that

  $E(X + Y) = E(X) + E(Y)$ ②

Now $\overline{X} = \frac{1}{n}(X_1 + \ldots + X_n)$

So: $E(\overline{X}) = \frac{1}{n}E(X_1 + \ldots + X_n)$ by ①

      $= \frac{1}{n}[E(X_1) + \ldots + E(X_n)]$ by ②

      $= \frac{1}{n}[\mu + \ldots + \mu]$

      $= \frac{n\mu}{n}$

That is: $E(\overline{X}) = \mu$

> You can extend formula ② by multiple applications – consider:
> $E((X_1 + X_2) + X_3)$
> $= E(X_1 + X_2) + E(X_3)$
> $= E(X_1) + E(X_2) + E(X_3)$

Example 5 shows that if we use the sample mean $\overline{X}$ as an estimator for μ then 'on average' it will give us the correct result. This is an important property for an estimator to have and you say that $\overline{X}$ is an **unbiased estimator** of μ. (So a specific value of $\overline{x}$ will provide an **unbiased estimate** of μ.)

■ If a statistic T is used as an estimator for a population parameter θ and E(T) = θ then T is an unbiased estimator for θ.

It seems obvious that being unbiased is a desirable feature to have in an estimator, but not all estimators possess this property. In Example 4 you found two statistics based on samples of size 3 from a population of counters of which 60% had the number 0 and 40% had the number 1. The population mean μ was $\frac{2}{5}$ and the population mode was 0 (since 60% of the counters had 0 on them). The two statistics that you calculated were the sample mean $\overline{X}$ and the sample mode M. You could use either of them as estimators for μ, the population mean, but you saw that $E(\overline{X}) = \mu$ but $E(M) \neq \mu$ so you would prefer to use the sample mean $\overline{X}$ rather than the sample mode M as an estimator for μ in this case. How about an estimator for the population mode? Neither of the statistics that you calculated had the property of being unbiased since $E(\overline{X}) = \mu = \frac{2}{5}$ and $E(M) = \frac{44}{125}$ whereas the population mode was 0.

Intuitively you might prefer the estimator M since it is, after all, a mode and is also slightly closer to the population mode. In this case you refer to M as a **biased estimator** for the population mode. The **bias** is simply the expected value of the estimator minus the parameter of the population it is estimating.

■ **If a statistic T is used as an estimator for a population parameter θ then the bias = $E(T) - \theta$**

In this case the bias is $\frac{44}{125}$.

So far you have found an unbiased estimator for μ, but how would you find an estimator for σ?

Before answering this question you need to find $\mathrm{Var}(\overline{X})$.

Example 6

A random sample $X_1, X_2, \ldots, X_n$ is taken from a population with $X \sim N(\mu, \sigma^2)$.

Show that $\mathrm{Var}(\overline{X}) = \dfrac{\sigma^2}{n}$

In Chapter 8 of book S1 an important property of variances was given:
$$\mathrm{Var}(aX) = a^2\,\mathrm{Var}(X) \qquad \text{①}$$
Also in Chapter 1 of this book you saw that
$$\mathrm{Var}(X + Y) = \mathrm{Var}(X) + \mathrm{Var}(Y) \text{ if } X \text{ and } Y \text{ are independent} \qquad \text{②}$$

Now $\qquad \overline{X} = \dfrac{1}{n}(X_1 + \ldots + X_n)$

$$\mathrm{Var}(\overline{X}) = \frac{1}{n^2}\,\mathrm{Var}(X_1 + \ldots + X_n) \qquad \text{by ①}$$

$$= \frac{1}{n^2}[\mathrm{Var}(X_1) + \ldots + \mathrm{Var}(X_n)] \qquad \text{by ②}$$

$$= \frac{1}{n^2}[\sigma^2 + \ldots + \sigma^2]$$

$$= \frac{n\sigma^2}{n^2}$$

That is: $\mathrm{Var}(\overline{X}) = \dfrac{\sigma^2}{n}$

This result will be referred to again later in Section 3.3.

Example 7

Show that $S^2 = \dfrac{1}{n-1}\sum(X - \overline{X})^2 = \dfrac{1}{n-1}\left(\sum X^2 - n\overline{X}^2\right)$ is an unbiased estimator for σ^2.

In order to find $E(S^2)$ you need to recall certain facts about expected values and variances. These are:

$$\sigma^2 = \text{Var}(X) = E(X^2) - \mu^2$$

so: $\qquad E(X^2) = \sigma^2 + \mu^2 \qquad\qquad\qquad ①$

and $\qquad \text{Var}\,(\overline{X}) = \dfrac{\sigma^2}{n}$ and $E(\overline{X}) = \mu$

See Examples 5 and 6.

so: $\qquad \dfrac{\sigma^2}{n} = E(\overline{X}^2) - \mu^2$

and $\qquad E(\overline{X}^2) = \dfrac{\sigma^2}{n} + \mu^2 \qquad\qquad ②$

So $\qquad S^2 = \dfrac{1}{n-1}\left(\sum X^2 - n\overline{X}^2\right)$

then $\qquad E(S^2) = \dfrac{1}{n-1} E\left(\sum X^2 - n\overline{X}^2\right)$

$\qquad\qquad = \dfrac{1}{n-1}\left[E\left(\sum X^2\right) - nE(\overline{X}^2)\right]$

Using
$E(aX - bY) = aE(X) - bE(Y)$.

But $\quad E\left(\sum X^2\right) = \sum E(X^2) = nE(X^2)$

Since each X_i has the same distribution as X.

so: $\qquad E(S^2) = \dfrac{n}{n-1}\left[E(X^2) - E(\overline{X}^2)\right]$

$\qquad\qquad = \dfrac{n}{n-1}\left[\sigma^2 + \mu^2 - \left(\dfrac{\sigma^2}{n} + \mu^2\right)\right]$ by ① and ②

That is: $\quad E(S^2) = \sigma^2$

and so the statistic S^2 is an unbiased estimator of the population variance σ^2. It is because of this property of S^2 that we use s^2 to estimate σ^2 in calculations where a value of σ^2 is not known.

Sometimes the 'hat notation' is used to describe an estimator of a parameter and $\hat{\theta}$ **represents an estimator of** θ.

So you might use $\hat{\mu}$ to represent an estimator of μ, usually you have $\hat{\mu} = \bar{x}$.

Similarly you sometimes use $\hat{\sigma}^2$ to represent an estimator of σ^2. Following on from Example 7, you usually have $S^2 = \hat{\sigma}^2$.

Example 8

The table below summarises the number of breakdowns, x, on a town's bypass on 30 randomly chosen days.

Number of breakdowns	2	3	4	5	6	7	8	9
Number of days	3	5	4	3	5	4	4	2

Calculate unbiased estimates of the mean and variance of the number of breakdowns.

By calculator: $\sum x = 160$ and $\sum x^2 = 990$

So $\hat{\mu} = \bar{x} = \dfrac{160}{30} = 5.33$

and $\hat{\sigma}^2 = s_x^2 = \dfrac{990 - 30\bar{x}^2}{29} = 4.7126 = 4.71 \ (3 \ \text{s.f.})$

You can use your calculator to find these values but it is recommended that you show them in the appropriate formulae.

The working shown here is recommended when answering questions of this type.

Example 9

The random variable X has a continuous uniform distribution defined over the range $[0, \alpha]$. A random sample $X_1, X_2, ..., X_n$, is taken .

a Show that $\bar{X}$ is a biased estimator for α and state the bias.

b Suggest a suitable unbiased estimator for α.

a Since $X \sim U[0, \alpha] \ \mu = E(X) = \dfrac{\alpha}{2}$

Since $E(\bar{X}) = \mu$

Then $E(\bar{X}) = \dfrac{\alpha}{2}$

so $\bar{X}$ is a biased estimator of α

The bias $= E(\bar{X}) - \alpha = \dfrac{\alpha}{2} - \alpha = -\dfrac{\alpha}{2}$

b If Y is an unbiased estimator of α then

$E(Y) = \alpha$.

Since $E(\bar{X}) = \dfrac{\alpha}{2}$, a sensible statistic for Y is $Y = 2\bar{X}$

See the S2 part of the formula book where the formulae for mean and variance of a continuous uniform distribution are given.

See Example 5. $E(\bar{X}) = \mu$ for *any* sample.

Use the definition of bias from page 28.

This is the definition of an unbiased estimator.

Exercise 3B

1 Find unbiased estimates of the mean and variance of the populations from which the following random samples have been taken.

a 21.3; 19.6; 18.5; 22.3; 17.4; 16.3; 18.9; 17.6; 18.7; 16.5; 19.3; 21.8; 20.1; 22.0

b 1; 2; 5; 1; 6; 4; 1; 3; 2; 8; 5; 6; 2; 4; 3; 1

c 120.4; 230.6; 356.1; 129.8; 185.6; 147.6; 258.3; 329.7; 249.3

d 0.862; 0.754; 0.459; 0.473; 0.493; 0.681; 0.743; 0.469; 0.538; 0.361.

2 Find unbiased estimates of the mean and the variance of the populations from which random samples with the following summaries have been taken.

a $n = 120$ $\sum x = 4368$ $\sum x^2 = 162\,466$

b $n = 30$ $\sum x = 270$ $\sum x^2 = 2546$

c $n = 1037$ $\sum x = 1140.7$ $\sum x^2 = 1278.08$

d $n = 15$ $\sum x = 168$ $\sum x^2 = 1913$

3 The concentrations, in mg per litre, of a trace element in 7 randomly chosen samples of water from a spring were:

240.8   237.3   236.7   236.6   234.2   233.9   232.5.

Determine unbiased estimates of the mean and the variance of the concentration of the trace element per litre of water from the spring.   **E**

4 Cartons of orange are filled by a machine. A sample of 10 cartons selected at random from the production contained the following quantities of orange (in ml).

201.2   205.0   209.1   202.3   204.6
206.4   210.1   201.9   203.7   207.3

Calculate unbiased estimates of the mean and variance of the population from which this sample was taken.   **E**

5 A manufacturer of self-assembly furniture required bolts of two lengths, 5 cm and 10 cm, in the ratio 2 : 1 respectively.

a Find the mean μ and the variance σ^2 for the lengths of bolts in this population.

A random sample of three bolts is selected from a large box containing bolts in the required ratio.

b List all possible samples.

c Find the sampling distribution for the mean $\overline{X}$.

d Hence find $E(\overline{X})$ and $Var(\overline{X})$.

e Find the sampling distribution for the mode M.

f Hence find $E(M)$ and $Var(M)$.

g Find the bias when M is used as an estimator of the population mode.

6 A biased six-sided die has probability p of landing on a six.

Every day, for a period of 25 days, the die is rolled 10 times and the number of sixes X is recorded giving rise to a sample $X_1, X_2, ..., X_{25}$.

a Write down $E(X)$ in terms of p.

b Show that the sample mean $\overline{X}$ is a biased estimator of p and find the bias.

c Suggest a suitable unbiased estimator of p.

7 The random variable $X \sim U[-\alpha, \alpha]$.

a Find $E(X)$ and $E(X^2)$.

A random sample X_1, X_2, X_3 is taken and the statistic $Y = X_1^2 + X_2^2 + X_3^2$ is calculated.

b Show that Y is an unbiased estimator of α^2.

3.3 **You need to be able to use the standard error of the mean.**

So far you have seen how to find unbiased estimators for μ and σ^2. A little thought will show that, for a sample $X_1, X_2, ..., X_n$, $E(X_i) = \mu$, for every value of i. So why should you bother to calculate the mean $\overline{X}$ when *any* member of the sample has the same property; that it provides an unbiased estimator for the mean μ? To answer this question you need to look back at Examples 5 and 6 where some important properties of the estimator $\overline{X}$ were found

$$E(\overline{X}) = \mu \text{ and } \text{Var}(\overline{X}) = \frac{\sigma^2}{n}$$

Notice that $\overline{X}$ is always an unbiased estimator of μ but also that, as the sample size n increases, the variance of this estimator *decreases*. It is this property of $\text{Var}(\overline{X})$ that makes $\overline{X}$ a useful estimator of μ and certainly a better estimator than X_1 or any other single member of the sample, since a smaller variance means that the values of any estimates should be closer to the required value μ. (This principle is examined further in S4.)

The variance of an estimator is clearly a helpful guide about how useful a particular estimate may be. In calculations you often want to find the standard deviation of the estimator, and this is referred to as the **standard error** of the estimator. So if the estimator is the mean $\overline{X}$ then the standard error of the mean is $\frac{\sigma}{\sqrt{n}}$. Since, in practice, you often have to use s^2 instead of σ^2, the standard error of the mean is used to refer to either $\frac{\sigma}{\sqrt{n}}$ or $\frac{s}{\sqrt{n}}$ if σ is not known.

- **Standard error of the mean is $\frac{\sigma}{\sqrt{n}}$ or $\frac{s}{\sqrt{n}}$**

Example 10

(This is an extension of Example 8)

The table below summarises the number of breakdowns, x, on a town's bypass on 30 randomly chosen days.

Number of breakdowns	2	3	4	5	6	7	8	9
Number of days	3	5	4	3	5	4	4	2

a Calculate unbiased estimates of the mean and variance of the number of breakdowns.

Twenty more days were randomly sampled and this sample had a mean of 6.0 days and $s^2 = 5.0$.

b Treating the 50 results as a single sample, obtain further unbiased estimates of the population mean and variance.

c Find the standard error of this new estimate of the mean.

d Estimate the size of sample required to achieve a standard error of less than 0.25.

a By calculator:

$$\sum x = 160 \text{ and } \sum x^2 = 990$$

So $\hat{\mu} = \overline{x} = \dfrac{160}{30} = 5.33$

and $\hat{\sigma}^2 = s_x{}^2 = \dfrac{990 - 30\overline{x}^2}{29}$

$$= 4.7126 = 4.71 \text{ (3 s.f.)}$$

These calculations were completed in Example 8.

b New sample: $\bar{y} = 6.0 \Rightarrow \sum y = 20 \times 6.0 = 120$

$$s_y^2 = 5.0 \Rightarrow \frac{\sum y^2 - 20 \times 6^2}{19} = 5$$

So: $\sum y^2 = 5 \times 19 + 20 \times 36$

i.e. $\sum y^2 = 815$

> First you need to 'unwrap' the formulae for y and s_y^2 to find $\sum y$ and $\sum y^2$.

So the combined sample (w) of size 50 has

$$\sum w = 160 + 120 = 280$$

$$\sum w^2 = 990 + 815 = 1805$$

> Now combine with $\sum x$ and $\sum x^2$. Let the combined variable be w.

Then the combined estimate of μ is

$$\bar{w} = \frac{280}{50} = 5.6$$

and the estimate for σ^2 is

$$s_w^2 = \frac{1805 - 50 \times 5.6^2}{49}$$

i.e. $s_w^2 = 4.8367\ldots = 4.84$ (3 s.f.)

c The best estimate of σ^2 will be s_w^2 since it is based on a larger sample than s_x^2 or s_y^2.

So the standard error is $\dfrac{s_w}{\sqrt{50}} = \sqrt{\dfrac{4.836\ldots}{50}} = 0.311$

> Use the $\dfrac{s}{\sqrt{n}}$ formula for standard error.

d To achieve a standard error < 0.25 you require

$$\sqrt{\frac{4.836\ldots}{n}} < 0.25$$

that is: $\sqrt{n} > \dfrac{\sqrt{4.8367\ldots}}{0.25}$

$$\sqrt{n} > 8.797\ldots$$

$$n > 77.38$$

So we need a sample of at least 78.

> You do not know the value for σ so you will have to use your best estimate of it, namely s_w.

Exercise 3C

1 John and Mary each independently took a random sample of sixth-formers in their college and asked them how much money, in pounds, they earned last week. John used his sample of size 20 to obtain unbiased estimates of the mean and variance of the amount earned by a sixth-former at their college last week. He obtained values of $\bar{x} = 15.5$ and $s_x^2 = 8.0$.

Mary's sample of size 30 can be summarised as $\sum y = 486$ and $\sum y^2 = 8222$.

a Use Mary's sample to find unbiased estimates of μ and σ^2.

b Combine the samples and use all 50 observations to obtain further unbiased estimates of μ and σ^2.

c Find the standard error of the mean for each of these estimates of μ.

d Comment on which estimate of μ you would prefer to use.

2 A machine operator checks a random sample of 20 bottles from a production line in order to estimate the mean volume of bottles (in cm³) from this production run. The 20 values can be summarised as $\sum x = 1300$ and $\sum x^2 = 84\,685$.

a Use this sample to find unbiased estimates of μ and σ^2.

A supervisor knows from experience that the standard deviation of volumes on this process, σ, should be 3 cm³ and he wishes to have an estimate of μ that has a standard error of less than 0.5 cm³.

b What size sample will he need to achieve this?

The supervisor takes a further sample of size 16 and finds $\sum x = 1060$.

c Combine the two samples to obtain a revised estimate of μ.

3 The heights of certain seedlings after growing for 10 weeks in a greenhouse have a standard deviation of 2.6 cm. Find the smallest sample that must be taken for the standard error of the mean to be less than 0.5 cm.

4 The hardness of a plastic compound was determined by measuring the indentation produced by a heavy pointed device.

The following observations in tenths of a millimetre were obtained:

4.7, 5.2, 5.4, 4.8, 4.5, 4.9, 4.5, 5.1, 5.0, 4.8.

a Estimate the mean indentation for this compound.

b Estimate the standard error of the mean.

c Estimate the size of sample required in order that in future the standard error of the mean should be just less than 0.05.

5 Prospective army recruits receive a medical test. The probability of each recruit passing the test is p, independent of any other recruit. The medicals are carried out over two days and on the first day n recruits are seen and on the next day $2n$ are seen. Let X_1 be the number of recruits who pass the test on the first day and let X_2 be the number passing on the second day.

a Write down $E(X_1)$, $E(X_2)$, $Var(X_1)$ and $Var(X_2)$.

b Show that $\dfrac{X_1}{n}$ and $\dfrac{X_2}{2n}$ are both unbiased estimates of p and state, giving a reason, which you would prefer to use.

c Show that $X = \frac{1}{2}\left(\dfrac{X_1}{n} + \dfrac{X_2}{2n}\right)$ is an unbiased estimator of p.

d Show that $Y = \left(\dfrac{X_1 + X_2}{3n}\right)$ is an unbiased estimator of p.

e Which of the statistics $\dfrac{X_1}{n}, \dfrac{X_2}{2n}, X$ or Y is the best estimator of p?

The statistic $T = \left(\dfrac{2X_1 + X_2}{3n}\right)$ is proposed as an estimator of p.

f Find the bias.

6 Two independent random samples $X_1, X_2, \ldots, X_n$ and $Y_1, Y_2, \ldots, Y_m$ are taken from a population with mean μ and variance σ^2. The unbiased estimators $\overline{X}$ and $\overline{Y}$ of μ are calculated. A new unbiased estimator T of μ is sought of the form $T = r\overline{X} + s\overline{Y}$.

a Show that, since T is unbiased, $r + s = 1$.

b By writing $T = r\overline{X} + (1 - r)\overline{Y}$, show that

$$\text{Var}(T) = \sigma^2 \left[\frac{r^2}{n} + \frac{(1 - r)^2}{m} \right]$$

c Show that the minimum variance of T is when $r = \dfrac{n}{n + m}$.

d Find the best (in the sense of minimum variance) estimator of μ of the form $r\overline{X} + s\overline{Y}$.

---

7 A large bag of counters has 40% with the number 0 on, 40% with the number 2 on and 20% with the number 1.

a Find the mean μ, and the variance σ^2, for this population of counters.

A random sample of size 3 is taken from the bag.

b List all possible samples.

c Find the sampling distribution for the mean $\overline{X}$.

d Find $E(\overline{X})$ and $\text{Var}(\overline{X})$.

e Find the sampling distribution for the median N.

f Hence find $E(N)$ and $\text{Var}(N)$.

g Show that N is an unbiased estimator of μ.

h Explain which estimator, $\overline{X}$ or N, you would choose as an estimator of μ.

3.4 You need to be able to use the **Central Limit Theorem** to find an approximation to the sampling distribution of $\overline{X}$.

Example 11

A random sample $X_1, X_2, \ldots, X_n$ is taken from a population where $X \sim N(\mu, \sigma^2)$

Show that $\overline{X} \sim N\left(\mu, \dfrac{\sigma^2}{n}\right)$.

$X_1 + X_2 \sim N(2\mu, 2\sigma^2)$ Use the results from Chapter 1.

$\sum X = X_1 + \ldots + X_n \sim N(n\mu, n\sigma^2)$ Extend the above results.

$\overline{X} = \frac{1}{n}\sum X$ and we have seen that

$E(\overline{X}) = \mu$ and $\text{Var}(\overline{X}) = \dfrac{\sigma^2}{n}$ See Example 5 and Example 6.

So, since the population is normal we know that $\overline{X}$ will be normal too and therefore $\overline{X} \sim N\left(\mu, \dfrac{\sigma^2}{n}\right)$

Example 11 has shown that if the distribution of the population is known to be normal then the sampling distribution of $\overline{X}$ is normal too. However, in many cases the distribution of the population is not known or it is clearly not normal so what will the distribution of $\overline{X}$ be when the population from which the sample was taken does *not* have a normal distribution? The answer, in general, is that it depends upon the distribution of the population and in most cases there is no easy way of describing the distribution of $\overline{X}$. However, there is an important result that enables you to say something about the distribution of $\overline{X}$ when the sample size n is large. This result is known as the **Central Limit Theorem** and it tells you that when n is large $\overline{X}$ is approximately normally distributed, whether or not the *population* is normally distributed.

■ **The Central Limit Theorem says that if $X_1, X_2, ..., X_n$ is a random sample of size n from a population with mean μ and variance σ^2 then $\overline{X}$ is approximately $\sim N\left(\mu, \dfrac{\sigma^2}{n}\right)$**

This theorem is very important in statistics and is one of the main reasons why the normal distribution is so useful. The theorem is an approximation but the approximation improves as n, the sample size, increases; this is another reason (remember $Var(\overline{X})$ gets smaller as n increases) why a large sample is often desirable.

A proof of this theorem is beyond the scope of this course, but the following example should help you to see why it might be true.

Example 12

A table of random digits is designed so that the value, R, of a digit comes from a discrete uniform distribution over the set $\{0, 1, 2, 3, 4, 5, 6, 7, 8, 9\}$

a Find $\mu = E(R)$.

b Using the first row of the table on page 139 take a sample of size 10.

c Calculate the sample mean.

a By symmetry $E(R) = 4.5$ ──────── Use $\frac{1}{2}(0 + 9)$.

b The first 10 random digits are:

$8, 6, 1, 3, 8, 4, 1, 0, 0, 7$

c So: $\overline{x} = \dfrac{38}{10}$

$= 3.8$

Notice that the sample has some high (e.g. 8) and some low (e.g. 0) digits but that the high and low values tend to cancel each other out so that the mean value for the sample is close to the mean for the population as a whole. It is therefore much more unlikely that you would get a mean $\overline{x}$ of 0 or 8 than a value close to μ. It is this 'cancelling out' effect of taking a mean that might lead you to expect the distribution of $\overline{X}$ to peak close to μ and tail off at each end.

It is a worthwhile experiment to repeat this sampling of random numbers and obtain a large number of observations of $\overline{X}$. A histogram of these $\overline{x}$ values can be plotted and a shape approximating to a normal distribution should result. This can be done on a calculator or a computer.

Example 13

A sample of size 9 is taken from a population with distribution $N(10, 2^2)$. Find the probability that the sample mean $\overline{X}$ is more than 11.

The population is normal, so $\overline{X}$ will have a normal distribution despite the small size of the sample.

$$\text{Var}(\overline{X}) = \frac{\sigma^2}{n} = \frac{2^2}{9} = \left(\frac{2}{3}\right)^2$$

So: $\qquad \overline{X} \sim N\left(10, \left(\frac{2}{3}\right)^2\right).$

The mean of $\overline{X}$ is 10 and the standard deviation is $\frac{2}{3}$ so:

$$P(\overline{X} > 11) = P\left(Z > \frac{11 - 10}{\frac{2}{3}}\right)$$

$$= P(Z > 1.5)$$

$$= 1 - 0.9332$$

$$= 0.0668$$

> The mean of $\overline{X}$ is μ (=10) and the variance of $\overline{X}$ is $\frac{\sigma^2}{n}$.

> Use $Z = \frac{Y - \mu}{\sigma}$.

Example 14

A cubical die is relabelled so that there are three faces marked 1, two faces marked 3 and one marked 6. The die is rolled 40 times and the mean of the 40 scores is recorded.
Find an approximation for the probability that the mean is over 3.

Let the random variable X = the score on a single roll; then the distribution of X is

X:	1	3	6
$p(x)$:	$\frac{1}{2}$	$\frac{1}{3}$	$\frac{1}{6}$

So: $\quad \mu = E(X) = \sum xP(X = x) = 1 \times \frac{1}{2} + 3 \times \frac{1}{3} + 6 \times \frac{1}{6}$

$$= 2.5$$

and $\sigma^2 = \text{Var}(X) = \sum x^2 P(X = x) - \mu^2$

$$= 1^2 \times \frac{1}{2} + 3^2 \times \frac{1}{3} + 6^2 \times \frac{1}{6} - \left(\frac{5}{2}\right)^2$$

$$= \frac{19}{2} - \frac{25}{4} = 3.25 \text{ or } \frac{13}{4}$$

Now by the Central Limit Theorem $\overline{X} \approx \sim N\left(2.5, \frac{13}{160}\right)$

So $\quad P(\overline{X} > 3) = P\left(Z > \frac{3 - 2.5}{\sqrt{\frac{13}{160}}}\right)$

$$= P(Z > 1.75)$$

$$= 1 - 0.9599$$

$$= 0.0401 \text{ or } 0.040 \text{ (3 d.p.)}$$

> Use the techniques for finding means and variances of discrete distributions you met in book S1.

> The population is clearly not normally distributed but the sample size ($n = 40$) is quite large so the Central Limit Theorem can be used.

It is worth pointing out that although the X_i and therefore $\overline{X}$ are discrete distributions, whereas the normal distribution is a continuous distribution, a continuity correction is not appropriate in this example. However, if you had been asked to find a probability for $\sum X$ such as $P(\sum X > 120)$, then a continuity correction as described in book S2 could be applied.

Exercise 3D

1 A sample of size 6 is taken from a normal distribution $N(10, 2^2)$.
What is the probability that the sample mean exceeds 12?

2 A machine fills cartons in such a way that the amount of drink in each carton is distributed normally with a mean of $40\,\text{cm}^3$ and a standard deviation of $1.5\,\text{cm}^3$.

   a A sample of four cartons is examined.
   Find the probability that the mean amount of drink is more than $40.5\,\text{cm}^3$.

   b A sample of 49 cartons is examined.
   Find the probability that the mean amount of drink is more than $40.5\,\text{cm}^3$ on this occasion.

3 The lengths of bolts produced by a machine have an unknown distribution with mean $3.03\,\text{cm}$ and standard deviation $0.20\,\text{cm}$.

   A sample of 100 bolts is taken.

   a Estimate the probability that the mean length of this sample is less than $3\,\text{cm}$.

   b What size sample is required if the probability that the mean is less than $3\,\text{cm}$ is to be less than 1%?

4 Forty observations are taken from a population with distribution given by the probability density function

$$f(x) = \begin{cases} \frac{2}{9}x, & 0 \leqslant x \leqslant 3, \\ 0, & \text{otherwise.} \end{cases}$$

   a Find the mean and variance of this population.

   b Find an estimate of the probability that the mean of the 40 observations is more than 2.10.

5 A fair die is rolled 35 times.

   a Find the approximate probability that the mean of the 35 scores is more than 4.

   b Find the approximate probability that the total of the 35 scores is less than 100.

6 The 25 children in a class each roll a fair die 30 times and record the number of sixes they obtain.
Find an estimate of the probability that the mean number of sixes recorded for the class is less than 4.5.

7 The error in mm made in measuring the length of a table has a uniform distribution over the range $[-5, 5]$. The table is measured 20 times.
Find an estimate of the probability that the mean error is less than $-1\,\text{mm}$.

8 Telephone calls arrive at an exchange at an average, rate of two per minute. Over a period of 30 days a telephonist records the number of calls that arrive in the five-minute period before her break.

   a Find an approximation for the probability that the total number of calls recorded is more than 350.

   b Estimate the probability that the mean number of calls in the five-minute interval is less than 9.0.

9 How many times must a fair die be rolled in order for there to be a less than 1% chance that the mean of all the scores differs from 3.5 by more than 0.1?

10 The heights of women in a certain area have a mean of 175 cm and a standard deviation of 2.5 cm. The heights of men in the same area have a mean of 177 cm and a standard deviation of 2.0 cm. Samples of 40 women and 50 men are taken and their heights are recorded. Find the probability that the mean height of the men is more than 3 cm greater than the mean height of the women.

11 A computer, in adding numbers, rounds each number off to the nearest integer. All the rounding errors are independent and come from a uniform distribution over the range $[-0.5, 0.5]$.

   a Given that 1000 numbers are added, find the probability that the total error is greater than $+10$.

   b Find how many numbers can be added together so that the probability that the magnitude of the total error is less than 10 is at least 0.95.

12 An electrical company repairs very large numbers of television sets and wishes to estimate the mean time taken to repair a particular fault. It is known from previous research that the standard deviation of the time taken to repair this particular fault is 2.5 minutes.

   The manager wishes to ensure that the probability that the estimate differs from the true mean by less than 30 seconds is 0.95.
   Find how large a sample is required. **E**

3.5 You need to be able to calculate confidence intervals for a population parameter.

You are now in a position to complete the estimation of μ, the population mean. In the previous sections we considered taking a random sample of n students and measuring their heights. Now we shall assume that the standard deviation of heights of students, i.e. σ, is known but the mean μ (in metres) is *not* known and this is the parameter we seek to estimate. Suppose the sample gave an estimate $\bar{x} = 1.73$. What can you say about μ?

You know that an estimate of μ is $\hat{\mu} = 1.73$, but it would be more helpful if you could give a range of values for μ and also provide some measure of how reliable this range of values is. People sometimes use phrases like 'I'm 90% (or 99% or 95%) certain that I left the keys on the kitchen table'. In statistics we use the properties of the standard normal distribution, $N(0, 1^2)$, to formalise this idea, and arrive at a range of values for μ about which we are, say, 95% confident.

Example 15

Show that a 95% confidence interval for μ, based on a sample of size n, is given by

$$\bar{x} \pm 1.96 \times \frac{\sigma}{\sqrt{n}}$$

$\overline{X}$ is approximately $\sim N\left(\mu, \frac{\sigma^2}{\sqrt{n}}\right)$

and therefore

$$Z = \frac{\overline{X} - \mu}{\frac{\sigma}{\sqrt{n}}} \sim N(0, 1^2)$$

Whatever the distribution of the population you know by the Central Limit Theorem that $\overline{X}$ will be approximately normal.

Using the table on page 130 you can see that for the $N(0, 1^2)$ distribution

$$P(Z > 1.9600) = P(Z < -1.9600) = 0.025$$

and so 95% of the distribution is between -1.9600 and 1.9600

So $P(-1.96 < Z < 1.96) = 0.95$

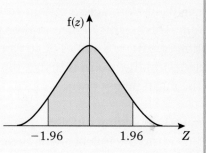

i.e. $P\left(-1.96 < \dfrac{\overline{X} - \mu}{\frac{\sigma}{\sqrt{n}}} < 1.96\right) = 0.95$

Look at the inequality inside the probability statement:

$$-1.96 \times \frac{\sigma}{\sqrt{n}} < \bar{x} - \mu < 1.96 \times \frac{\sigma}{\sqrt{n}}$$

$$-1.96 \times \frac{\sigma}{\sqrt{n}} - \bar{x} < \mu < 1.96 \times \frac{\sigma}{\sqrt{n}} - \bar{x}$$

$$\bar{x} + 1.96 \times \frac{\sigma}{\sqrt{n}} > \mu > \bar{x} - 1.96 \times \frac{\sigma}{\sqrt{n}}$$

$$\bar{x} - 1.96 \times \frac{\sigma}{\sqrt{n}} < \mu < \bar{x} + 1.96 \times \frac{\sigma}{\sqrt{n}}$$

So the 95% confidence interval for μ is

$$\bar{x} \pm 1.96 \times \frac{\sigma}{\sqrt{n}}$$

Start to isolate μ.

Multiply by -1 and change the inequality.

The upper and lower values of a confidence interval are sometimes called the **confidence limits**.

In general we have the following formula:

■ **The 95% confidence interval for μ is**

$$\bar{x} \pm 1.96 \times \frac{\sigma}{\sqrt{n}}$$

You should notice that the 95% level of confidence gives rise to the value of 1.96 in the formula. So, again using the table on page 130, a 99% confidence interval would have the 1.96 replaced by 2.5758 so that a 99% confidence interval is given by

$$\bar{x} \pm 2.5758 \times \frac{\sigma}{\sqrt{n}}$$

Interpreting confidence intervals

- First, it is important to remember that μ is a fixed, but unknown, number and as such it cannot vary and does *not* have a *distribution*.

> So it does not make sense to talk about the probability that μ is between certain values.

- Secondly, it *is* worth remembering that we base a 95% confidence interval on a probability statement about the normal distribution $Z \sim N(0, 1^2)$.

> The choice of 95% gave rise to z values of ± 1.96 and, as you can see from the table on page 130, a 90% confidence interval would use z values of ± 1.6449 instead of ± 1.96.

- However, although you start by considering probabilities associated with the random variable Z, the final confidence interval does *not* tell you that the probability that μ lies inside the interval is 0.95. Rather, since μ is fixed, it is the *confidence interval* that varies (according to the value of $\bar{x}$).

- What a 95% confidence interval tells you is that the probability that the interval contains μ is 0.95. The diagram opposite illustrates the 95% confidence intervals calculated from different samples and also shows the position of μ.

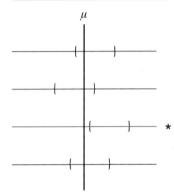

Suppose 20 samples of size 100 were taken and 95% confidence intervals for μ were calculated for each sample. This would give 20 different confidence intervals each based on one of the 20 different values of $\bar{x}$. If you imagine for a moment that you actually do know what the value of μ is then you can plot each of these confidence intervals on a diagram similar to the one here; you would expect that 95% of these confidence intervals would contain the value μ but about once in every 20 times you would get an interval which did not contain μ (like the one marked * here). The problem for the statistician is that he or she never knows whether the confidence interval they have just calculated is one that contains μ or not.

> The choice of what level of confidence to use in a particular situation will depend on the problem involved but a value of 95% is commonly used if no other value is specified.

However, 95% (or 90% or 99% depending on the degree of confidence required) of the time they will be right!

Example 16

The breaking strains of reels of string produced at a certain factory have a standard deviation of 1.5 kg. A sample of 100 reels from a certain batch were tested and their mean breaking strain was 5.30 kg.

a Find a 95% confidence interval for the mean breaking strain of string in this batch.

The manufacturer becomes concerned if the lower 95% confidence limit falls below 5 kg. A sample of 80 reels from another batch gave a mean breaking strain of 5.31 kg.

> The two end values in a confidence interval are sometimes called the **confidence limits**.

b Will the manufacturer be concerned?

The distribution for breaking strains is not known but the sample is quite large and by the Central Limit Theorem $\bar{X}$ will be approximately normally distributed.

> Sometimes a question might ask you for the significance of the Central Limit Theorem to your calculations.

a 95% confidence interval (C.I.) is

$$\bar{x} \pm 1.96 \times \frac{\sigma}{\sqrt{n}} = 5.30 \pm 1.96 \times \frac{1.5}{\sqrt{100}}$$

$$= (5.006, 5.594)$$

Use the $\bar{x} \pm 1.96 \times \frac{\sigma}{\sqrt{n}}$ formula.

b Lower 95% confidence limit is

$$\bar{x} - 1.96 \times \frac{\sigma}{\sqrt{n}} = 5.31 - \frac{1.96 \times 1.5}{\sqrt{80}}$$

$$= 4.98$$

so the manufacturer will be concerned.

We are sometimes interested in the **width** of a confidence interval.

■ **The width of a confidence interval is the difference between the upper confidence limit and the lower confidence limit. This is $2 \times z \times \frac{\sigma}{\sqrt{n}}$, where z is the value from the tables, for example, 1.96, 1.6449, etc.**

There are three factors that affect the width: the value of σ, the size of the sample n and the degree of confidence required. In a particular example where σ and n are determined, the only factor you can change to alter the width is the degree of confidence. A high level of confidence (e.g. 99%) will give a greater width than a lower level of confidence (e.g. 90%) and the statistician has to weigh up the advantages of high confidence against greater width when calculating a confidence interval.

Example 17

A random sample of size 25 is taken from a normal population with standard deviation of 2.5. The mean of the sample was 17.8.

a Find a 99% C.I. for the population mean μ.

b What size sample is required to obtain a 99% C.I. of width of at most 1.5?

c What confidence level would be associated with the interval based on the above sample of 25 but of width 1.5, i.e.(17.05, 18.55)?

a 99% C.I. is

$$x \pm 2.5758 \times \frac{\sigma}{\sqrt{n}} = 17.8 \pm 2.5758 \times \frac{2.5}{\sqrt{25}}$$

$$= (16.51, 19.09)$$

Use the table on page 130 to find 2.5758.

b Width of 99% C.I. is $2 \times 2.5758 \times \frac{2.5}{\sqrt{n}}$

so you require $1.5 > \frac{12.879...}{\sqrt{n}}$

i.e. $n > 73.719...$

so you need $n = 74$

Use the $2 \times z \times \frac{\sigma}{\sqrt{n}}$ formula or the definition for the width.

c A width of 1.5 $\Rightarrow 1.5 = 2 \times z \times \dfrac{2.5}{\sqrt{25}}$

$$z = 1.5$$

From the table on page 129 you find that

$$P(Z < 1.5) = 0.9332$$

and so $P(Z > 1.5) = P(Z < -1.5)$

$$= 1 - 0.9332$$

$$= 0.0668$$

So the confidence level is $100 \times (1 - 2 \times 0.0668) = 86.6\%$.

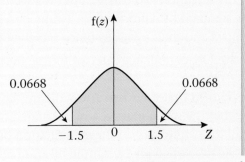

0.0668   0.0668

The percentage of the confidence interval is given by the area between $z = \pm 1.5$.

Exercise 3E

1 A random sample of size 9 is taken from a normal distribution with variance 36. The sample mean is 128.

a Find a 95% confidence interval for the mean μ of the distribution.

b Find a 99% confidence interval for the mean μ of the distribution.

2 A random sample of size 25 is taken from a normal distribution with standard deviation 4. The sample mean is 85.

a Find a 90% confidence interval for the mean μ of the distribution.

b Find a 95% confidence interval for the mean μ of the distribution.

3 A normal distribution has mean μ and variance 4.41. A random sample has the following values:

$$23.1, \quad 21.8, \quad 24.6, \quad 22.5.$$

Use this sample to find 98% confidence limits for the mean μ.

4 A normal distribution has standard deviation 15. Estimate the sample size required if the following confidence intervals for the mean should have width of less than 2.

a 90%   **b** 95%   **c** 99%

5 Repeat Question 4 for a normal distribution with standard deviation 2.4 and a desired width of less than 0.8.

6 An experienced poultry farmer knows that the mean weight μ kg for a large population of chickens will vary from season to season but the standard deviation of the weights should remain at 0.70 kg. A random sample of 100 chickens is taken from the population and the weight x kg of each chicken in the sample is recorded, giving $\sum x = 190.2$. Find a 95% confidence interval for μ.

7 A railway watchdog is studying the number of seconds that express trains are late in arriving. Previous surveys have shown that the standard deviation is 50. A random sample of 200 trains was selected and gave rise to a mean of 310 seconds late. Find a 90% confidence interval for the mean number of seconds that express trains are late.

8 An investigation was carried out into the total distance travelled by lorries in current use. The standard deviation can be assumed to be 15 000 km. A random sample of 80 lorries were stopped and their mean distance travelled was found to be 75 872 km.

Find a 90% confidence interval for the mean distance travelled by lorries in current use.

9 It is known that each year the standard deviation of the marks in a certain examination is 13.5 but the mean mark μ will fluctuate. An examiner wishes to estimate the mean mark of all the candidates on the examination but he only has the marks of a sample of 250 candidates which give a sample mean of 68.4.

a What assumption about these candidates must the examiner make in order to use this sample mean to calculate a confidence interval for μ?

b Assuming that the above assumption is justified, calculate a 95% confidence interval for μ.

Later the examiner discovers that the actual value of μ was 65.3.

c What conclusions might the examiner draw about his sample?

10 The number of hours for which an electronic device can retain information has a uniform distribution over the range $[\mu - 10, \mu + 10]$ but the value of μ is not known.

a Show that the variance of the number of hours the device can retain the information for is $\frac{100}{3}$.

A random sample of 120 devices were tested and the mean number of hours they retained information for was 78.7.

b Find a 95% confidence interval for μ.

11 A statistics student calculated a 95% and a 99% confidence interval for the mean μ of a certain population but failed to label them. The two intervals were (22.7, 27.3) and (23.2, 26.8).

a State, with a reason, which interval is the 95% one.

b Estimate the standard error of the mean in this case.

c What was the student's unbiased estimate of the mean μ in this case?

12 A 95% confidence interval for a mean μ is 85.3 ± 2.35. Find the following confidence intervals for μ.

a 90%   **b** 98%   **c** 99%

13 The managing director of a certain firm has commissioned a survey to estimate the mean expenditure of customers on electrical appliances. A random sample of 100 people were questioned and the research team presented the managing director with a 95% confidence interval of (£128.14, £141.86).

The director says that this interval is too wide and wants a confidence interval of total width £10.

a Using the same value of $\bar{x}$, find the confidence limits in this case.

b Find the level of confidence for the interval in part **a**.

The managing director is still not happy and now wishes to know how large a sample would be required to obtain a 95% confidence interval of total width no more than £10.

c Find the smallest size of sample that will satisfy this request.

14 A plant produces steel sheets whose weights are known to be normally distributed with a standard deviation of 2.4 kg. A random sample of 36 sheets had a mean weight of 31.4 kg. Find 99% confidence limits for the population mean. **E**

15 A machine is regulated to dispense liquid into cartons in such a way that the amount of liquid dispensed on each occasion is normally distributed with a standard deviation of 20 ml.

Find 99% confidence limits for the mean amount of liquid dispensed if a random sample of 40 cartons had an average content of 266 ml. **E**

16 a The error made when a certain instrument is used to measure the body length of a butterfly of a particular species is known to be normally distributed with mean 0 and standard deviation 1 mm. Calculate, to 3 decimal places, the probability that the error made when the instrument is used once is numerically less than 0.4 mm.

   b Given that the body length of a butterfly is measured 9 times with the instrument, calculate, to 3 decimal places, the probability that the mean of the 9 readings will be within 0.5 mm of the true length.

   c Given that the mean of the 9 readings was 22.53 mm, determine a 98% confidence interval for the true body length of the butterfly. **E**

3.6 You need to be able to test hypotheses about the mean of a normal distribution.

In book S2 you met the idea of a **hypothesis test** and a definition of it is given below.

■ **A hypothesis test about a population parameter θ tests a null hypothesis H_0, specifying a particular value for θ, against an alternative hypothesis H_1, which will indicate whether the test is one-tailed or two-tailed.**

In book S2 the parameters considered were the proportion p of a binomial distribution and the mean λ or μ of a Poisson distribution. In this section you will learn how to extend the idea to tests for μ, the mean, of a normal distribution. The process is similar to that of a trial in a courtroom. The null hypothesis is on trial, evidence is presented and the jury has to make a decision 'on the balance of probability'.

Example 18

A certain company sells fruit juice in cartons. The amount of juice in a carton has a normal distribution with a standard deviation of 3 ml.

The company claims that the mean amount of juice per carton, μ, is 60 ml. A trading inspector has received complaints that the company is overstating the mean amount of juice per carton and he wishes to investigate this complaint. The trading inspector took a random sample of 16 cartons which gave a mean of 59.1 ml.

Using a 5% level of significance, and stating your hypotheses clearly, test whether or not there is evidence to uphold this complaint.

The hypotheses are:

$$H_0: \mu = 60 \qquad H_1: \mu < 60$$

> Remember H_0 must specify a particular value of μ. The inspector therefore will assume that the company is innocent and wish to formulate a null hypothesis to express this idea in terms of the parameter μ.

> If the company is guilty then μ must be less than 60 (there would be few complaints if the cartons contained on average more than 60 ml) and so the alternative hypothesis H_1 is $H_1: \mu < 60$. **This means the test is one-tailed.**

This is like the 'evidence' presented at a trial.

The sample gives $n = 16$ and $\bar{x} = 59.1$

$$P(\bar{X} \leqslant 59.1 | \mu = 60) = P\left(Z \leqslant \frac{59.1 - 60}{\frac{3}{4}}\right)$$

$$= P(Z \leqslant -1.2)$$

$$= 0.1151$$

$0.1151 > 0.05$ so the result is not significant and there is insufficient evidence to reject H_0, that $\mu = 60$.

> The inspector (like the jury in a trial) then has to calculate the probability of obtaining evidence 'as bad or worse' than this, assuming that the null hypothesis is true.
> The alternative hypothesis is that the company is deceiving customers and that $\mu < 60$; the inspector's sample gave a mean of 59.1 and so any value of the sample mean *less than or equal to* 59.1 will be 'as bad or worse'.

> You know that $\bar{X} \sim N\left(\mu, \frac{\sigma^2}{n}\right)$ then standardise to use the tables.

> The conclusion should incorporate two statements:
> **1** State whether or not the test is significant.
> **2** Interpret this in the context of the question.

> This probability is greater than the 5% significance level so there is no reason to suspect the validity of H_0.

There is insufficient evidence to support the complaint.

Notice that the test was based on the statistic

$$Z = \frac{\bar{X} - 60}{\frac{3}{\sqrt{n}}}$$

> Recall that a statistic must not contain any unknown population parameters.

and this is the **test statistic** in this case.

■ **The test statistic in a test for the population mean μ is $Z = \dfrac{\bar{X} - \mu}{\frac{\sigma}{\sqrt{n}}}$ where μ is the value given by the null hypothesis and σ is given.**

It is sometimes helpful to consider what value z of the test statistic the inspector in Example 18 would have needed if he were to reject the hypothesis that $\mu = 60$. If you use a 5% significance level then (from table on p. 130):

$$P(Z \leqslant -1.6449) = 0.05$$

> A significant result is one where the null hypothesis is rejected. This is like a guilty verdict in a trial. The judge concludes that the probability of the defendant being innocent *and* evidence 'as bad or worse' as that presented is so small as to make it improbable that the assumption of innocence is sustainable.

so any value of $z \leqslant -1.6449$ would mean that the probability of obtaining a sample 'as bad or worse' is less than or equal to 5%, which is unlikely. This means that the assumption that H_0 is true is called into question and we *reject H_0 at the 5% level of significance*.

We call the region $Z \leqslant -1.6449$ the **critical region** of the statistic Z and the value -1.6449 is sometimes called the **critical value**.

■ **The critical region of a test statistic T is the range of values of T such that if the value of T, namely t, obtained from your particular sample lies in this critical region then you reject the null hypothesis.**

■ **The boundary value(s) of the critical region is (are) called the critical value(s).**

> You should note that in this case the critical values can be found so that the probability of lying in the critical region equals the significance level. In book S2 we were applying these ideas to discrete distributions and an exact match was usually not possible. The continuous nature of the normal distribution enables us to achieve this here.

In S3 tests for μ, the mean of a normal distribution are best carried out using the test statistic z and the critical region rather than calculating the probability.

Example 19

At a certain college new students are weighed when they join the college. The distribution of weights of students at the college when they enrol has a standard deviation of 7.5 kg and a mean of 70 kg. A random sample of 90 students from the new entry were weighed and their mean weight was 71.6 kg. Assuming that the standard deviation has not changed

a test, at the 5% level, whether there is evidence that the mean of the new entry is more than 70 kg.

b State the importance of the Central Limit Theorem to your test.

> Notice that the question does not say that the weights are normally distributed. You will have to invoke the Central Limit Theorem here and that is the reason for part **b**.

a $H_0 : \mu = 70$ $H_1 =: \mu > 70$ ──────── $\mu > 70$, so a one-tailed test is required.

$\sigma = 7.5$

A 5% significance level is required so the critical region for Z will be as shown by the diagram on the right.

From the table on page 130 this is $Z \geqslant 1.6449$.

The sample gives $n = 90$, $\bar{x} = 71.6$ and these give a value of the test statistic of

$$z = \frac{71.6 - 70}{\frac{7.5}{\sqrt{90}}} = 2.0239$$

This value *is* in the critical region, so you reject H_0 and conclude that there is evidence that the new class have a higher mean weight.

> Always give a conclusion in context.

b The Central Limit Theorem is used to assume that $\overline{X}$ (which is the mean weight of the 90 students) is normally distributed.

Example 20

A machine produces bolts of diameter D where D has a normal distribution with mean 0.580 cm and standard deviation 0.015 cm.

The machine is serviced and after the service a random sample of 50 bolts from the next production run is taken to see if the mean diameter of the bolts has changed from 0.580 cm. The distribution of the diameters of bolts after the service is still normal with a standard deviation of 0.015 cm. The mean diameter of the 50 bolts is 0.577 cm.

a Stating your hypotheses clearly test, at the 1% level, whether or not there is evidence that the mean diameter of the bolts has changed.

b Find the critical region for $\overline{X}$ in the above test.

> The word 'changed' in the question suggests that the alternative hypothesis is $\mu \neq 0.580$ so a two-tailed test is needed.

a $H_0: \mu = 0.580$ $H_1: \mu \neq 0.580$

   $\sigma = 0.015$

> There should be a value of σ given in the question.

A 1% significance test is required so the critical region for Z will be as shown by the diagram on the right.

From the table on page 130 the critical region of Z is

   $Z \leqslant -2.5758$ or $Z \geqslant 2.5758$.

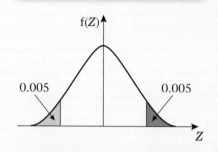

The sample gives $n = 50$, $\bar{x} = 0.577$ so the value of the test statistic is

$$z = \frac{0.577 - 0.580}{\frac{0.015}{\sqrt{50}}} = -1.414\ldots,$$

This is *not* in the critical region so you accept H_0 and conclude that there is no significant evidence that the mean diameter has changed.

> Always give your conclusion in context – mention 'mean diameter'.

b The critical region of Z is

   $Z \leqslant -2.5758$ or $Z \geqslant 2.5758$

So $Z = \dfrac{\overline{X} - 0.580}{\frac{0.015}{\sqrt{50}}} \leqslant -2.5758$

i.e. $\overline{X} \leqslant 0.580 - 2.5758 \times \dfrac{0.015}{\sqrt{50}} = 0.5745\ldots$

or $Z = \dfrac{\overline{X} - 0.580}{\frac{0.015}{\sqrt{50}}} \geqslant 2.5758$

i.e. $\overline{X} \geqslant 0.580 + 2.5758 \times \dfrac{0.015}{\sqrt{50}} = 0.5854\ldots.$

So the critical region for $\overline{X}$ is:

   $\overline{X} \leqslant 0.575$ or $\overline{X} \geqslant 0.585$

Note that $\bar{x} = 0.577$ does not lie in the critical region

> Use the critical regions for Z and the $Z = \dfrac{\overline{X} - \mu}{\frac{\sigma}{\sqrt{n}}}$ formula to form critical regions for $\overline{X}$.

> Notice that there is a similarity between a confidence interval and the critical region for a two-tailed hypothesis test. In this example the critical region was $\overline{X} \leqslant 0.575$ or $\overline{X} \geqslant 0.585$ and found from calculating $\mu \pm 2.5758 \times \dfrac{\sigma}{\sqrt{n}}$ and taking the region *outside*. The 99% confidence interval is simply (0.572, 0.582) and found by calculating $\bar{x} \pm 2.5758 \times \dfrac{\sigma}{\sqrt{n}}$ and taking the region *inside*. Notice that the critical region uses μ and the confidence interval uses $\bar{x}$.

The following four steps summarise the stages in answering questions about hypothesis tests for the mean μ.

1 Identify the sample mean $\bar{x}$ and value for the population mean μ given by the null hypothesis.

2 Write down the null (H_0) and alternative (H_1) hypotheses. The alternative hypothesis will determine whether you want a one-tailed or a two-tailed test.

3 Calculate the value of the test statistic $z = \dfrac{\bar{x} - \mu}{\frac{\sigma}{\sqrt{n}}}$.

4 Either using the critical region for Z, or by calculating a probability, complete the test and state your conclusions. The following points should be addressed.

    a Is the result significant or not?

    b What are the implications in terms of the *context of the original problem*?

Exercise 3F

In each of Questions 1–5 a random sample of size n is taken from a population having a normal distribution with mean μ and variance σ^2. Test the hypotheses at the stated levels of significance.

1 $H_0: \mu = 21$, $H_1: \mu \neq 21$, $n = 20$, $\bar{x} = 21.2$, $\sigma = 1.5$,   at the 5% level

2 $H_0: \mu = 100$, $H_1: \mu < 100$, $n = 36$, $\bar{x} = 98.5$, $\sigma = 5.0$,   at the 5% level

3 $H_0: \mu = 5$, $H_1: \mu \neq 5$, $n = 25$, $\bar{x} = 6.1$, $\sigma = 3.0$,   at the 5% level

4 $H_0: \mu = 15$, $H_1: \mu > 15$, $n = 40$, $\bar{x} = 16.5$, $\sigma = 3.5$,   at the 1% level

5 $H_0: \mu = 50$, $H_1: \mu \neq 50$, $n = 60$, $\bar{x} = 48.9$, $\sigma = 4.0$,   at the 1% level

In each of Questions 6–10 a random sample of size n is taken from a population having a $N(\mu, \sigma^2)$ distribution. Find the critical regions for the test statistic $\bar{X}$ in the following tests.

6 $H_0: \mu = 120$, $H_1: \mu < 120$, $n = 30$, $\sigma = 2.0$,   at the 5% level

7 $H_0: \mu = 12.5$, $H_1: \mu > 12.5$, $n = 25$, $\sigma = 1.5$,   at the 1% level

8 $H_0: \mu = 85$, $H_1: \mu < 85$, $n = 50$, $\sigma = 4.0$,   at the 10% level

9 $H_0: \mu = 0$, $H_1: \mu \neq 0$, $n = 45$, $\sigma = 3.0$,   at the 5% level

10 $H_0: \mu = -8$, $H_1: \mu \neq -8$, $n = 20$, $\sigma = 1.2$,   at the 1% level

11 The times taken for a capful of stain remover to remove a standard chocolate stain from a baby's bib are normally distributed with a mean of 185s and a standard deviation of 15s. The manufacturers of the stain remover claim to have developed a new formula which will shorten the time taken for a stain to be removed. A random sample of 25 capfuls of the new formula are tested and the mean time for the sample is 179s.

Test, at the 5% level, whether or not there is evidence that the new formula is an improvement.

12 The IQ scores of a population are normally distributed with a mean of 100 and standard deviation of 15. A psychologist wishes to test the theory that eating chocolate before sitting an IQ test improves your score. A random sample of 100 people are selected and they are each given a 100 g bar of chocolate to eat before taking a standard IQ test. Their mean score on the test was 102.5. Test the psychologist's theory at the 5% level.

13 The diameters of circular cardboard drinks mats produced by a certain machine are normally distributed with a mean of 9 cm and a standard deviation of 0.15 cm. After the machine is serviced a random sample of 30 mats is selected and their diameters are measured to see if the mean diameter has altered.

The mean of the sample was 8.95 cm. Test, at the 5% level, whether there is significant evidence of a change in the mean diameter of mats produced by the machine.

14 a Research workers measured the body lengths, in mm, of 10 specimens of fish spawn of a certain species off the coast of Eastern Scotland and found these lengths to be

$$12.5 \quad 10.2 \quad 11.1 \quad 9.6 \quad 12.1 \quad 9.3 \quad 10.7 \quad 11.4 \quad 14.7 \quad 10.4$$

Obtain unbiased estimates for the mean and variance of the lengths of all such fish spawn off Eastern Scotland.

b Research shows that, for a very large number of specimens of spawn of this species off the coast of Wales, the mean body length is 10.2 mm. Assuming that the variance of the lengths of spawn off Eastern Scotland is 2.56, perform a significance test at the 5% level to decide whether the mean body length of fish spawn off the coast of Eastern Scotland is larger than that of fish spawn off the coast of Wales. **E**

15 a Explain what you understand by the Central Limit Theorem.

b An electrical firm claims that the average lifetime of the bulbs it produces is 800 hours with a standard deviation of 42 hours. To test this claim a random sample of 120 bulbs was taken and these bulbs were found to have an average lifetime of 789 hours.

Stating your hypotheses clearly and using a 5% level of significance, test the claim made by the electrical firm. **E**

3.7 **You need to be able to test hypotheses about the difference between means of two independent normal distributions.**

If, instead of one population, you now have two independent populations then you can test hypotheses about the differences in the population means.

In Chapter 1 you saw that if X and Y are two independent normal distributions with means of μ_x and μ_y and standard deviations σ_x and σ_y respectively then

$$X - Y \sim N(\mu_x - \mu_y, \sigma_x^2 + \sigma_y^2)$$

Now if $\overline{X}$ and $\overline{Y}$ are sample means based on samples of size n_x and n_y respectively from the above two normal populations then:

$$\overline{X} - \overline{Y} \sim N\left(\mu_x - \mu_y, \frac{\sigma_x^2}{n_x} + \frac{\sigma_y^2}{n_y}\right)$$

and the statistic $\overline{X} - \overline{Y}$ can be used to test hypotheses about the values of μ_x and μ_y.

The Central Limit Theorem tells you that, provided the sample sizes n_x and n_y are large, then $\overline{X} - \overline{Y}$ will have a normal distribution whatever the distributions of X and Y. You can therefore use this to test if there is a significant difference between the means of any two populations. The usual null hypothesis is that the values of μ_x and μ_y are equal, but other situations are possible provided that the null hypothesis gives you a value for $\mu_x - \mu_y$.

The test statistic you will need to use is based upon the distribution of $\overline{X} - \overline{Y}$ and is

$$Z = \frac{\overline{X} - \overline{Y} - (\mu_x - \mu_y)}{\sqrt{\left(\dfrac{\sigma_x^2}{n_x} + \dfrac{\sigma_y^2}{n_y}\right)}}$$

This is given in the formula booklet.

■ **Test for difference between two means**

If $X \sim N(\mu_x, \sigma_x^2)$ and the independent random variable $Y \sim N(\mu_y, \sigma_y^2)$ then a test of the null hypothesis $H_0: \mu_x = \mu_y$ can be carried out using the test statistic

$$Z = \frac{\overline{X} - \overline{Y} - (\mu_x - \mu_y)}{\sqrt{\left(\dfrac{\sigma_x^2}{n_x} + \dfrac{\sigma_y^2}{n_y}\right)}} \sim N(0, 1^2)$$

If the sample sizes n_x and n_y are large then the result can be extended, by the Central Limit Theorem, to include cases where the distributions of X and Y are not normal.

Example 21

The weights of boys and girls in a certain school are known to be normally distributed with standard deviations of 5 kg and 8 kg respectively. A random sample of 25 boys had a mean weight of 48 kg and a random sample of 30 girls had a mean weight of 45 kg.

Stating your hypotheses clearly test, at the 5% level of significance, whether or not there is evidence that the mean weight of boys in the school is greater than the mean weight of the girls.

$H_0: \mu_{boy} = \mu_{girl}$ $\quad H_1: \mu_{boy} > \mu_{girl}$

$\sigma_1 = 5, n_1 = 25, \sigma_2 = 8$ and $n_2 = 30$:

The test statistic is $\quad z = \dfrac{\overline{x} - \overline{y} - (\mu_x - \mu_y)}{\sqrt{\dfrac{\sigma_x^2}{n_x} + \dfrac{\sigma_y^2}{n_y}}}$

$= \dfrac{48 - 45}{\sqrt{\dfrac{25}{25} + \dfrac{64}{30}}}$

$= \dfrac{3}{\sqrt{3.1333\ldots}}$

$= 1.6947\ldots$

The 5% (one-tailed) critical value for Z is $z = 1.6449$ (table on page 130) so this value is significant and you can reject H_0 and conclude that there is evidence that the mean weight of boys is greater than the mean weight of the girls.

The question you are asked is whether $\mu_{boy} > \mu_{girl}$. This will not yield a value for '$\mu_x - \mu_y$' so choose as your null hypothesis $\mu_{boy} = \mu_{girl}$. (In other words, if the mean weights are the *same*, does the sample provide evidence to contradict this assumption?)

Remember that from the null hypothesis you know $\mu_x - \mu_y = 0$.

Always quote the critical value from the tables in full and give your conclusion in context.

Sometimes you may be asked to test, for example, whether or not the mean weight of the boys exceeds the mean weight of the girls by more than 2 kg. The test would be similar to the above but the hypotheses will be slightly different and this will affect the test statistic.

Example 22

The weights of boys and girls in a certain school are known to be normally distributed with standard deviations of 5 kg and 8 kg respectively. A random sample of 25 boys had a mean weight of 48 kg and a random sample of 30 girls had a mean weight of 45 kg.

Stating your hypotheses clearly test, at the 5% level of significance, whether or not there is evidence that the mean weight of boys in the school is more than 2 kg greater than the mean weight of the girls.

$H_0: \mu_{boy} - \mu_{girl} = 2 \qquad H_1: \mu_{boy} - \mu_{girl} > 2$

Notice the null hypothesis still gives you a value for $\mu_x - \mu_y$.

$\sigma_1 = 5$, $n_1 = 25$, $\sigma_2 = 8$ and $n_2 = 30$:

Test statistic is

$$z = \frac{\bar{x} - \bar{y} - (\mu_x - \mu_y)}{\sqrt{\dfrac{\sigma_x^2}{n_x} + \dfrac{\sigma_y^2}{n_y}}}$$

Notice how the test statistic calculation has changed. This 2 comes from $\mu_x - \mu_y$.

$$= \frac{48 - 45 - 2}{\sqrt{\dfrac{25}{25} + \dfrac{64}{30}}}$$

$$= 0.565$$

The 5% (one-tailed) critical value for Z is $z = 1.6449$ (table on page 130) so this value is not significant.

There is insufficient evidence that the mean weight of the boys is more than 2 kg more than the mean weight of the girls.

Example 23

A manufacturer of personal stereos can use batteries made by two different manufacturers. The standard deviation of lifetimes for *Never Die* batteries is 3.1 hours and for *Everlasting* batteries it is 2.9 hours. A random sample of 80 *Never Die* batteries and a random sample of 90 *Everlasting* batteries were tested and their mean lifetimes were 7.9 hours and 8.2 hours respectively.

Stating your hypotheses clearly test, at the 5% level of significance, whether there is evidence of a difference between the mean lifetimes of the two makes of batteries.

Let μ_x be the mean lifetime of *Never Die* batteries and let μ_y be the mean lifetime of *Everlasting* batteries.

$H_0: \mu_x = \mu_y \qquad H_1: \mu_x \neq \mu_y$

$\sigma_x = 3.1$, $n_x = 80$, $\sigma_y = 2.9$ and $n_y = 90$

$\bar{x} - \bar{y} = 7.9 - 8.2 = -0.3$

So $z = \dfrac{\bar{x} - \bar{y} - (\mu_x - \mu_y)}{\sqrt{\dfrac{\sigma_x^2}{n_x} + \dfrac{\sigma_y^2}{n_y}}}$

$= \dfrac{-0.3}{\sqrt{\left(\dfrac{(3.1)^2}{80} + \dfrac{(2.9)^2}{90}\right)}}$

$= -0.649\ldots$

The 5% (two-tailed) critical values for Z are $z = \pm 1.9600$.

So this value is not significant and you do not reject H_0. You can conclude that there is no significant evidence of a difference in the mean lifetimes of the two makes of battery.

> Notice that you are looking for a *difference*, so a two-tailed test is appropriate.

> You are not told that the distributions of life times of batteries are normally distributed but the sample sizes are both quite large and so by the Central Limit Theorem you can proceed with $\bar{X} - \bar{Y}$ approximately normally distributed.

> From the null hypothesis you know that $\mu_x - \mu_y = 0$.

Exercise 3G

In Questions 1–3 carry out a test on the given hypotheses at the given level of significance. The populations from which the random samples are drawn are normally distributed.

1 $H_0: \mu_1 = \mu_2$, $H_1: \mu_1 > \mu_2$, $n_1 = 15$, $\sigma_1 = 5.0$, $n_2 = 20$, $\sigma_2 = 4.8$, $\bar{x}_1 = 23.8$ and $\bar{x}_2 = 21.5$ using a 5% level

2 $H_0: \mu_1 = \mu_2$, $H_1: \mu_1 \neq \mu_2$, $n_1 = 30$, $\sigma_1 = 4.2$, $n_2 = 25$, $\sigma_2 = 3.6$, $\bar{x}_1 = 49.6$ and $\bar{x}_2 = 51.7$ using a 5% level

3 $H_0: \mu_1 = \mu_2$, $H_1: \mu_1 < \mu_2$, $n_1 = 25$, $\sigma_1 = 0.81$, $n_2 = 36$, $\sigma_2 = 0.75$, $\bar{x}_1 = 3.62$ and $\bar{x}_2 = 4.11$ using a 1% level

In Questions 4–6 carry out a test on the given hypotheses at the given level of significance. What is the significance of the Central Limit Theorem in these three questions?

4 $H_0: \mu_1 = \mu_2$, $H_1: \mu_1 \neq \mu_2$, $n_1 = 85$, $\sigma_1 = 8.2$, $n_2 = 100$, $\sigma_2 = 11.3$, $\bar{x}_1 = 112.0$ and $\bar{x}_2 = 108.1$ using a 1% level

5 $H_0: \mu_1 = \mu_2$, $H_1: \mu_1 > \mu_2$, $n_1 = 100$, $\sigma_1 = 18.3$, $n_2 = 150$, $\sigma_2 = 15.4$, $\bar{x}_1 = 72.6$ and $\bar{x}_2 = 69.5$ using a 5% level

6 $H_0: \mu_1 = \mu_2$, $H_1: \mu_1 < \mu_2$, $n_1 = 120$, $\sigma_1 = 0.013$, $n_2 = 90$, $\sigma_2 = 0.015$, $\bar{x}_1 = 0.863$ and $\bar{x}_2 = 0.868$ using a 1% level

7 A certain factory has two machines designed to cut piping. The first machine works to a standard deviation of 0.011 cm and the second machine has a standard deviation of 0.015 cm. A random sample of 10 pieces of piping from the first machine has a mean length of 6.531 cm and a random sample of 15 pieces from the second machine has a length of 6.524 cm. Assuming that the lengths of piping follow a normal distribution, test, at the 5% level, whether or not the machines are producing piping of the same mean length.

3.8 You need to be able to test hypotheses and find confidence intervals for large samples.

One of the practical difficulties that you will encounter with these tests, and also in finding confidence intervals, is the need to know the value of the standard deviation. In practice, if you do not know μ, it is unlikely that you will know σ. Sometimes it is reasonable to assume that a manufacturing process will have the same standard deviation but perhaps just have an altered mean. Occasionally you can look at historical data and see that over a period of time the standard deviation has been constant, and it may be reasonable to assume that it remains so but often it may be impossible to say what σ is.

You saw earlier in this chapter (page 28–29) how to find an unbiased estimate for σ^2, namely s^2, and if you do not know σ then estimating it by s would seem a sensible idea. Your test statistic for a single sample would then be

$$\frac{\overline{x} - \mu}{\frac{s}{\sqrt{n}}}$$

Unfortunately, this statistic does not have a normal distribution. However, in situations where the distribution of the parent population is normal the distribution of this statistic is known and it is called Student's t distribution. This distribution is covered in S4.

If the sample size is very large the estimate, s, that you are using for σ might reasonably be expected to be very close to σ and, given that a more precise test would almost certainly involve a level of knowledge

There is no simple answer to the question how large a sample must be, other than 'the larger the better'.

beyond the scope of this book, for very large samples the above statistic is usually *assumed* to have an approximate N(0, 1^2) distribution. You must remember that such a test is an approximation and you should be wary of drawing strong conclusions from values of z close to the critical values.

■ **If the population is normal, or can be assumed to be so, then, for large samples, the statistic**

$$\frac{X - \mu}{\frac{s}{\sqrt{n}}}$$ **has an approximate N(0, 1^2) distribution.**

■ **If the population is not normal, by assuming that s is a close approximation to σ, then**

$$\frac{X - \mu}{\frac{s}{\sqrt{n}}}$$ **can be treated as having an approximate N(0, 1^2) distribution.**

These results can be used for hypothesis tests and confidence intervals.

Example 24

As part of a study into the health of young schoolchildren a random sample of 220 children from area A and a second, independent random sample of 180 children from area B were weighed. The results are given in the table below:

	n	$\bar{x}$	s
Area A	220	37.8	3.6
Area B	180	38.6	4.1

a Test, at the 5% level, of significance, whether or not there is evidence of a difference in the mean weight of children in the two areas. State your hypotheses clearly.

b State an assumption you have made in carrying out this test.

c Explain the significance of the Central Limit Theorem to this test.

a $H_0: \mu_A = \mu_B$ $H_1: \mu_A \neq \mu_B$

State the hypotheses in terms of μ. The word 'difference' suggests a two-tailed test.

Test statistic $\quad z = \dfrac{\bar{x}_A - \bar{x}_B - (\mu_A - \mu_B)}{\sqrt{\dfrac{\sigma_A^2}{n_A} + \dfrac{\sigma_B^2}{n_B}}}$

For a two-tailed test you can choose whether to use $\bar{x}_A - \bar{x}_B$ or $\bar{x}_B - \bar{x}_A$. It is usually easier to choose the case which gives a positive value to the test statistic, $\bar{x}_B - \bar{x}_A$ in this case.

$z = \dfrac{38.6 - 37.8}{\sqrt{\dfrac{3.6^2}{220} + \dfrac{4.1^2}{180}}}$

$z = 2.0499\ldots$

$= 2.05\ (3\ \text{s.f.})$

Give the value to at least 3 s.f.

2-tail 5% critical values are $z = \pm 1.96$

Always state the critical value(s).

Since $2.05 > 1.96$, the result is significant, so reject H_0.

There is evidence that the mean weight of children in the two areas is different.

Always give your conclusion in context.

b The test statistic requires σ so you have to assume that $s^2 = \sigma^2$ for both samples.

c You are not told that the populations are normally distributed but the samples are both large and so the Central Limit Theorem enables us to assume that $\overline{X}_A$ and $\overline{X}_B$ are both normal.

Note that the Central Limit Theorem is not an assumption – it is a theorem that can be used to enable you to use the normal distribution.

The assumption that $s^2 = \sigma^2$ is reasonable since both samples are large.

Exercise 3H

1 An experiment was conducted to compare the drying properties of two paints, Quickdry and Speedicover. In the experiment, 200 similar pieces of metal were painted, 100 randomly allocated to Quickdry and the rest to Speedicover.

The table below summarises the times, in minutes, taken for these pieces of metal to become touch-dry.

	Quickdry	Speedicover
Mean	28.7	30.6
Standard deviation	7.32	3.51

Using a 5% significance level, test whether or not the mean time for Quickdry to become touch-dry is less than that for Speedicover. State your hypotheses clearly. **E**

2 A supermarket examined a random sample of 80 weekend shoppers' purchases and an independent random sample of 120 weekday shoppers' purchases. The results are summarised in the table below.

	n	$\bar{x}$	s
Weekend	80	38.64	6.59
Weekday	120	40.13	8.23

a Stating your hypotheses clearly test, at the 5% level of significance, whether there is evidence that the mean expenditure in the week is more than at weekends.

b State an assumption you have made in carrying out this test.

3 It is claimed that the masses of components produced in a small factory have a mean mass of l0 g. A random sample of 250 of these components is tested and the sample mean, $\bar{x}$, is 9.88 g and the standard deviation, s, is 1.12 g.

a Test, at the 5% level, whether or not there has been change in the mean mass of a component.

b State any assumptions you would make to carry out this test.

4 Two independent samples are taken from population A and population B. Carry out the following tests using the information given.

a $H_0: \mu_A = \mu_B$, $H_1: \mu_A < \mu_B$ using a 1% level of significance
$n_A = 90$, $n_B = 110$, $\bar{x}_A = 84.1$, $\bar{x}_B = 87.9$, $s_A = 12.5$, $s_B = 14.6$

b $H_0: \mu_A - \mu_B = 2$, $H_1: \mu_A - \mu_B > 2$ using a 5% level of significance
$n_A = 150$, $n_B = 200$, $\bar{x}_A = 125.1$, $\bar{x}_B = 119.3$, $s_A = 23.2$, $s_B = 18.4$

c State an assumption that you have made in carrying out these tests.

5 A shopkeeper complains that the average weight of chocolate bars of a certain type that he is buying from a wholesaler is less than the stated value of 85.0 g. The shopkeeper weighed 100 bars from a large delivery and found that their weights had a mean of 83.6 g and a standard deviation of 7.2 g. Using a 5% significance level, determine whether or not the shopkeeper is justified in his complaint. State clearly the null and alternative hypotheses that you are using, and express your conclusion in words. **E**

6 A certain health authority set up an investigation to examine the ages of mothers when they give birth to their first children.

A random sample of 250 first-time mothers from a certain year had a mean age of 22.45 years with a standard deviation of 2.9 years. A further random sample of 280 first-time mothers taken 10 years later had a mean age of 22.96 years with a standard deviation of 2.8 years.

a Test whether or not these figures suggest that there is a difference in the mean age of first-time mothers between these two dates. Use a 5% level of significance.

b State any assumptions you have made about the distribution of ages of first-time mothers.

Mixed exercise　31

1 The breaking stresses of rubber bands are normally distributed.

A company uses bands with a mean breaking stress of 46.50 N.

A new supplier claims that they can supply bands that are stronger and provides a sample of 100 bands for the company to test. The company checked the breaking stress, x, for each of these 100 bands and the results are summarised as follows:

$$n = 100 \qquad \sum x = 4715 \qquad \sum x^2 = 222\,910$$

a Test, at the 5% level, whether or not there is evidence that the new bands are better.

b Find an approximate 95% confidence interval for the mean breaking stress of these new rubber bands.

2 On each of 100 days a conservationist took a sample of 1 litre of water from a particular place along a river, and measured the amount, x mg, of chlorine in the sample. The results she obtained are shown in the table.

x	1	2	3	4	5	6	7	8	9
Number of days	4	8	20	22	16	13	10	6	1

a Calculate the mean amount of chlorine present per litre of water, and estimate, to 3 decimal places, the standard error of this mean.

b Obtain approximate 98% confidence limits for the mean amount of chlorine present per litre of water.

Given that measurements at the same point under the same conditions are taken for a further 100 days,

c estimate, to 3 decimal places, the probability that the mean of these measurements will be greater than 4.6 mg per litre of water.　**E**

3 The amount, to the nearest mg, of a certain chemical in particles in the atmosphere at a meteorological station was measured each day for 300 days. The results are shown in the table.

Amount of chemical (mg)	12	13	14	15	16
Number of days	5	42	210	31	12

Find the mean daily amount of chemical over the 300 days and estimate, to 2 decimal places, its standard error.

4 From time to time a firm manufacturing pre-packed furniture needs to check the mean distance between pairs of holes drilled by machine in pieces of chipboard to ensure that no change has occurred. It is known from experience that the standard deviation of the distance is 0.43 mm. The firm intends to take a random sample of size n, and to calculate a 99% confidence interval for the mean of the population. The width of this interval must be no more than 0.60 mm.

Calculate the minimum value of n. **E**

5 The times taken by five-year-old children to complete a certain task are normally distributed with a standard deviation of 8.0s. A random sample of 25 five-year-old children from school A were given this task and their mean time was 44.2s.

a Find 95% confidence limits for the mean time taken by five-year-old children from school A to complete this task.

The mean time for a random sample of 20 five-year-old children from school B was 40.9 s. The headteacher of school B concluded that the overall mean for school B must be less than that of school A. Given that the two samples were independent,

b test the headteacher's conclusion using a 5% significance level. State your hypotheses clearly. **E**

6 The random variable X has a normal distribution with mean μ and standard deviation 2.

A random sample of 25 observations is taken and the sample mean $\overline{X}$ is calculated in order to test the null hypothesis $\mu = 7$ against the alternative hypothesis $\mu > 7$ using a 5% level of significance.

Find the critical region for $\overline{X}$. **E**

7 A certain brand of mineral water comes in bottles. The amount of water in a bottle, in millilitres, follows a normal distribution of mean μ and standard deviation 2. The manufacturer claims that μ is 125. In order to maintain standards the manufacturer takes a sample of 15 bottles and calculates the mean amount of water per bottle to be 124.2 millilitres.

Test, at the 5% level, whether or not there is evidence that the value of μ is lower than the manufacturer's claim. State your hypotheses clearly. **E**

8 The random variable X is normally distributed with mean μ and variance σ^2.

a Write down the distribution of the sample mean $\overline{X}$ of a random sample of size n.

An efficiency expert wishes to determine the mean time taken to drill a fixed number of holes in a metal sheet.

b Determine how large a random sample is needed so that the expert can be 95% certain that the sample mean time will differ from the true mean time by less than 15 seconds. Assume that it is known from previous studies that $\sigma = 40$ seconds. **E**

9 A commuter regularly uses a train service which should arrive in London at 0931. He decided to test this stated arrival time. Each working day for a period of 4 weeks he recorded the number of minutes x that the train was late on arrival in London. If the train arrived early then the value of x was negative. His results are summarised as follows:

$$n = 20 \qquad \sum x = 15.0 \qquad \sum x^2 = 103.21$$

a Calculate unbiased estimates of the mean and variance of the number of minutes late of his train service.

The random variable X represents the number of minutes that the train is late on arriving in London. Records kept by the railway company show that over fairly short periods, the standard deviation of X is 2.5 minutes. The commuter made 2 assumptions about the distribution of X and the values obtained in the sample and went on to calculate a 95% confidence interval for the mean arrival time of this train service.

b State the two assumptions.

c Find the confidence interval.

d Given that the assumptions are reasonable, comment on the stated arrival time of the service.

E

10 The random variable X is normally distributed with mean μ and variance σ^2.

a Write down the distribution of the sample mean $\overline{X}$ of a random sample of size n.

b Explain what you understand by a 95% confidence interval.

A garage sells both leaded and unleaded petrol. The distribution of the values of sales for each type is normal. During 1990 the standard deviation of individual sales of each type of petrol is £3.25. The mean of the individual sales of leaded petrol during this time is £8.72. A random sample of 100 individual sales of unleaded petrol gave a mean of £9.71.

Calculate

c an interval within which 90% of the sales of leaded petrol will lie,

d a 95% confidence interval for the mean sales of unleaded petrol.

The mean of the sales of unleaded petrol for 1989 was £9.10.

e Using a 5% significance level, investigate whether there is sufficient evidence to conclude that the mean of all the 1990 unleaded sales was *greater* than the mean of the 1989 sales.

f Find the size of the sample that should be taken so that the garage proprietor can be 95% certain that the sample mean of sales of unleaded petrol during 1990 will differ from the true mean by less than 50p.

E

11 **a** Explain what is meant by a 98% confidence interval for a population mean.

The lengths, in cm, of the leaves of willow trees are known to be normally distributed with variance $1.33\,\text{cm}^2$.

A sample of 40 willow tree leaves is found to have a mean of 10.20 cm.

b Estimate, giving your answer to 3 decimal places, the standard error of the mean.

c Use this value to estimate symmetrical 95% confidence limits for the mean length of the population of willow tree leaves, giving your answer to 2 decimal places.

d Find the minimum size of the sample of leaves which must be taken if the width of the symmetrical 98% confidence interval for the population mean is at most 1.50 cm.

E

12 The distance driven by a long distance lorry driver in a week is a normally distributed variable having mean 1130 km and standard deviation 106 km.

a Find, to 3 decimal places, the probability that in a given week he will drive less than 1000 km.

b Find, to 3 decimal places, the probability that in 20 weeks his average distance driven per week is more than 1200 km.

New driving regulations are introduced and, in the first 20 weeks after their introduction, he drives a total of 21 900 km.

Assuming that the standard deviation of the weekly distances he drives is unchanged,

c test, at the 10% level of significance, if his mean weekly driving distance has been reduced. State clearly your null and alternative hypotheses. **E**

13 Climbing rope produced by a manufacturer is known to be such that one-metre lengths have breaking strengths that are normally distributed with mean 170.2 kg and standard deviation 10.5 kg. Find, to 3 decimal places, the probability that

a a one-metre length of rope chosen at random from those produced by the manufacturer will have a breaking strength of 175 kg to the nearest kg,

b a random sample of 50 one-metre lengths will have a mean breaking strength of more than 172.4 kg.

A new component material is added to the ropes being produced. The manufacturer believes that this will increase the mean breaking strength without changing the standard deviation. A random sample of 50 one-metre lengths of the new rope is found to have a mean breaking strength of 172.4 kg.

c Perform a significance test at the 5% level to decide whether this result provides sufficient evidence to confirm the manufacturer's belief that the mean breaking strength is increased. State clearly the null and alternative hypotheses that you are using. **E**

14 A machine fills 1 kg packets of sugar. The actual weight of sugar delivered to each packet can be assumed to be normally distributed. The manufacturer requires that,

i the mean weight of the contents of a packet is 1010 g, and

ii 95% of all packets filled by the machine contain between 1000 g and 1020 g of sugar.

a Show that this is equivalent to demanding that the variance of the sampling distribution, to 2 decimal places, is equal to 26.03 g^2.

A sample of 8 packets was selected at random from those filled by the machine. The weights, in grams, of the contents of these packets were

    1012.6   1017.7   1015.2   1015.7   1020.9   1005.7   1009.9   1011.4.

Assuming that the variance of the actual weights is 26.03 g^2,

b test at the 2% significance level, (stating clearly the null and alternative hypotheses that you are using) to decide whether this sample provides sufficient evidence to conclude that the machine is not fulfilling condition **i**. **E**

15 **a** Write down the mean and the variance of the distribution of the means of all possible samples of size n taken from an infinite population having mean μ and variance σ^2.

b Describe the form of this distribution of sample means when

    i n is large,

    ii the distribution of the population is normal.

The standard deviation of all the till receipts of a supermarket during 1984 was £4.25.

c Given that the mean of a random sample of 100 of the till receipts is £18.50, obtain an approximate 95% confidence interval for the mean of all the till receipts during 1984.

d Find the size of sample that should be taken so that the management can be 95% confident that the sample mean will not differ from the true mean by more than 50p.

e The mean of all the till receipts of the supermarket during 1983 was £19.40. Using a 5% significance level, investigate whether the sample in **a** above provides sufficient evidence to conclude that the mean of all the 1984 till receipts is different from that in 1983. **E**

16 The diameters of eggs of the little gull are approximately normally distributed with mean 4.11 cm and standard deviation 0.19 cm.

a Calculate the probability that an egg chosen at random has a diameter between 3.9 cm and 4.5 cm.

A sample of 8 little gull eggs was collected from a particular island and their diameters, in cm, were

$$4.4, \quad 4.5, \quad 4.1, \quad 3.9, \quad 4.4, \quad 4.6, \quad 4.5, \quad 4.1$$

Assuming that the standard deviation of the diameters of eggs from the island is also 0.19 cm,

b test, at the 1% level, whether the results indicate that the mean diameter of little gull eggs on this island is different from elsewhere. **E**

17 Records of the diameters of spherical ball bearings produced on a certain machine indicate that the diameters are normally distributed with mean 0.824 cm and standard deviation 0.046 cm. Two hundred samples, each consisting of 100 ball bearings, are chosen.

a Calculate the expected number of the 200 samples having a mean diameter less than 0.823 cm.

On a certain day it was suspected that the machine was malfunctioning. It may be assumed that if the machine is malfunctioning it will change the mean of the diameters without changing their standard deviation. On that day a random sample of 100 ball bearings had mean diameter of 0.834 cm.

b Determine a 98% confidence interval for the mean diameter of the ball bearings being produced that day.

c Hence state whether or not you would conclude that the machine is malfunctioning on that day given that the significance level is 2%. **E**

Summary of key points

1   Unbiased estimators

$\overline{X} = \dfrac{\sum X}{n}$ is an unbiased estimator of the population mean μ.

$S^2 = \dfrac{\sum X^2 - n\overline{X}^2}{n-1}$ is an unbiased estimator of the population variance σ^2.

2   The Central Limit Theorem

states that if the sample size n is large then $X \approx\sim \mathrm{N}\!\left(\mu, \dfrac{\sigma^2}{n}\right)$ no matter what the distribution of the population.

3   Confidence intervals

A 95% confidence interval for the population mean μ is given by

$$\overline{x} \pm 1.96 \times \frac{\sigma}{\sqrt{n}}$$

where the 1.96 comes from the normal tables and relates to the confidence level.

4   Hypothesis tests (single sample)

The test statistic for a hypothesis test of the population mean μ based on a single sample is

$$z = \frac{\overline{x} - \mu}{\dfrac{\sigma}{\sqrt{n}}}$$

5   Hypothesis tests (two independent samples)

The test statistic for a hypothesis test about the values of population means μ_x and μ_y is

$$z = \frac{\overline{x} - \overline{y} - (\mu_x - \mu_y)}{\sqrt{\dfrac{\sigma_x^2}{n_x} + \dfrac{\sigma_y^2}{n_y}}}$$

6   Large samples

If the sample size is large then s^2 is often assumed to be equal to σ^2.

Review Exercise

1 The time, in minutes, it takes Robert to complete the puzzle in his morning newspaper each day is normally distributed with mean 18 and standard deviation 3. After taking a holiday, Robert records the times taken to complete a random sample of 15 puzzles and he finds that the mean time is 16.5 minutes. You may assume that the holiday has not changed the standard deviation of times taken to complete the puzzle.

Stating your hypotheses clearly test, at the 5% level of significance, whether or not there has been a reduction in the mean time Robert takes to complete the puzzle. **E**

2 In a trial of diet A a random sample of 80 participants were asked to record their weight loss, x kg, after their first week of using the diet. The results are summarised by

$$\sum x = 361.6 \quad \text{and} \quad \sum x^2 = 1753.95.$$

a Find unbiased estimates for the mean and variance of weight lost after the first week of using diet A.

The designers of diet A believe it can achieve a greater mean weight loss after the first week than a standard diet B. A random sample of 60 people used diet B. After the first week they had achieved a mean weight loss of 4.06 kg, with an unbiased estimate of variance of weight loss of $2.50 \, \text{kg}^2$.

b Test, at the 5% level of significance, whether or not the mean weight loss after the first week using diet A is greater than that using diet B. State your hypotheses clearly.

c Explain the significance of the Central Limit Theorem to the test in part **b**.

d State an assumption you have made in carrying out the test in part **b**. **E**

3 A random sample of the daily sales (in £s) of a small company is taken and, using tables of the normal distribution, a 99% confidence interval for the mean daily sales is found to be

$$(123.5, 154.7).$$

Find a 95% confidence interval for the mean daily sales of the company. **E**

4 A set of scaffolding poles come in two sizes, long and short. The length L of a long pole has the normal distribution $N(19.7, 0.5^2)$. The length S of a short pole has the normal distribution $N(4.9, 0.2^2)$. The random variables L and S are independent. A long pole and a short pole are selected at random.

a Find the probability that the length of the long pole is more than 4 times the length of the short pole.

Four short poles are selected at random and placed end to end in a row. The random variable T represents the length of the row.

b Find the distribution of T.

c Find $P(|L - T| < 0.1)$. **E**

5 Describe one advantage and one disadvantage of

a quota sampling,

b simple random sampling. **E**

6 A report on the health and nutrition of a population stated that the mean height of three-year-old children is 90 cm and the standard deviation is 5 cm. A sample of 100 three-year-old children was chosen from the population.

a Write down the approximate distribution of the sample mean height. Give a reason for your answer.

b Hence find the probability that the sample mean height is at least 91 cm. **E**

7 A machine produces metal containers. The weights of the containers are normally distributed. A random sample of 10 containers from the production line was weighed, to the nearest 0.1 kg, and gave the following results

49.7,	50.3,	51.0,	49.5,	49.9
50.1,	50.2,	50.0,	49.6,	49.7.

a Find unbiased estimates of the mean and variance of the weights of the population of metal containers.

The machine is set to produce metal containers whose weights have a population standard deviation of 0.5 kg.

b Estimate the limits between which 95% of the weights of metal containers lie.

c Determine the 99% confidence interval for the mean weight of metal containers. **E**

8 A school has 15 classes and a sixth form. In each class there are 30 students. In the sixth form there are 150 students. There are equal numbers of boys and girls in each class. There are equal numbers of boys and girls in the sixth form. The headteacher wishes to obtain the opinions of the students about school uniforms.

Explain how the headteacher would take a stratified sample of size 40. **E**

9 A workshop makes two types of electrical resistor.

The resistance, X ohms, of resistors of Type A is such that $X \sim N(20, 4)$.

The resistance, Y ohms, of resistors of Type B is such that $Y \sim N(10, 0.84)$.

When a resistor of each type is connected into a circuit, the resistance R ohms of the circuit is given by $R = X + Y$ where X and Y are independent.

Find

a $E(R)$,   **b** $Var(R)$,

c $P(28.9 < R < 32.64)$. **E**

10 The drying times of paint can be assumed to be normally distributed. A paint manufacturer paints 10 test areas with a new paint. The following drying times, to the nearest minute, were recorded.

82,	98,	140,	110,	90,
125,	150,	130,	70,	110.

a Calculate unbiased estimates for the mean and the variance of the population of drying times of this paint.

Given that the population standard deviation is 25,

b find a 95% confidence interval for the mean drying time of this paint.

Fifteen similar sets of tests are done and the 95% confidence interval is determined for each set.

c Estimate the expected number of these 15 intervals that will enclose the true value of the population mean μ. **E**

11 Some biologists were studying a large group of wading birds. A random sample of 36 were measured and the wing length, x mm, of each wading bird was recorded. The results are summarised as follows.

$$\sum x = 6046, \qquad \sum x^2 = 1\,016\,338.$$

a Calculate unbiased estimates of the mean and the variance of the wing lengths of these birds.

Given that the standard deviation of the wing lengths of this particular type of bird is actually 5.1 mm,

b find a 99% confidence interval for the mean wing length of the birds from this group. **E**

12 The weights of adult men are normally distributed with a mean of 84 kg and a standard deviation of 11 kg.

a Find the probability that the total weight of 4 randomly chosen adult men is less than 350 kg.

The weights of adult women are normally distributed with a mean of 62 kg and a standard deviation of 10 kg.

b Find the probability that the weight of a randomly chosen adult man is less than one and a half times the weight of a randomly chosen adult woman. **E**

13 A researcher is hired by a cleaning company to survey the opinions of employees on a proposed pension scheme. The company employs 55 managers and 495 cleaners.

To collect data the researcher decides to give a questionnaire to the first 50 cleaners to leave at the end of the day.

a Give 2 reasons why this method is likely to produce biased results.

b Explain briefly how the researcher could select a sample of 50 employees using

i a systematic sample,

ii a stratified sample.

Using the random number tables in the formulae book, and starting with the top left hand corner (8) and working across, 50 random numbers between 1 and 550 inclusive were selected. The first two suitable numbers are 384 and 100.

c Find the next two suitable numbers. **E**

14 A sociologist is studying how much junk food teenagers eat. A random sample of 100 female teenagers and an independent random sample of 200 male teenagers were asked to estimate what their weekly expenditure on junk food was. The results are summarised below.

	n	mean	s.d.
Female teenagers	100	£5.48	£3.62
Male teenagers	200	£6.86	£4.51

a Using a 5% significance level, test whether or not there is a difference in the mean amounts spent on junk food by male teenagers and female teenagers. State your hypotheses clearly.

b Explain briefly the importance of the Central Limit Theorem in this problem. **E**

15 a State two reasons why stratified sampling might be chosen as a method of sampling when carrying out a statistical survey.

b State one advantage and one disadvantage of quota sampling. **E**

16 A sample of size 5 is taken from a population that is normally distributed with mean 10 and standard deviation 3.

Find the probability that the sample mean lies between 7 and 10. **E**

17 A computer company repairs large numbers of PCs and wants to estimate the mean time to repair a particular fault. Five repairs are chosen at random from the company's records and the times taken, in seconds, are

205 310 405 195 320.

a Calculate unbiased estimates of the mean and the variance of the population of repair times from which this sample has been taken.

It is known from previous results that the standard deviation of the repair time for this fault is 100 seconds. The company manager wants to ensure that there is a probability of at least 0.95 that the estimate of the population mean lies within 20 seconds of its true value.

b Find the minimum sample size required. **E**

18 The random variable D is defined as
$$D = A - 3B + 4C$$
where $A \sim N(5, 2^2)$, $B \sim N(7, 3^2)$ and $C \sim N(9, 4^2)$, and A, B and C are independent.

a Find $P(D < 44)$.

The random variables B_1, B_2 and B_3 are independent and each has the same distribution as B. The random variable X is defined as

$$X = A - \sum_{i=1}^{3} B_i + 4C.$$

b Find $P(X > 0)$. **E**

19 A manufacturer produces two flavours of soft drink, cola and lemonade. The weights, C and L, in grams, of randomly selected cola and lemonade cans are such that $C \sim N(350, 8)$ and $L \sim N(345, 17)$.

a Find the probability that the weights of two randomly selected cans of cola will differ by more than 6 g.

One can of each flavour is selected at random.

b Find the probability that the can of cola weighs more than the can of lemonade.

Cans are delivered to shops in boxes of 24 cans. The weights of empty boxes are normally distributed with mean 100 g and standard deviation 2 g.

c Find the probability that a full box of cola cans weighs between 8.51 kg and 8.52 kg.

d State an assumption you made in your calculation in part **c**. **E**

After completing this chapter you should be able to:

- form hypotheses about how well a distribution fits as a model for an observed frequency distribution
- calculate the measure of goodness of fit
- understand what is meant by degrees of freedom
- work out the number of degrees of freedom
- know the chi-squared (χ^2) family of distributions and be able to select the appropriate distribution
- apply goodness of fit tests for the discrete distributions, including the discrete uniform, binomial and Poisson distributions
- apply goodness of fit tests for the continuous distributions including the continuous uniform and Normal distributions
- know what is meant by a contingency table
- apply goodness of fit to contingency tables.

Goodness of fit and contingency tables

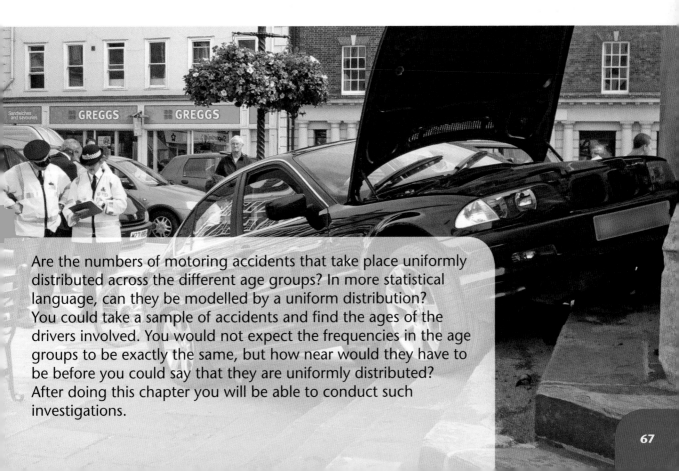

Are the numbers of motoring accidents that take place uniformly distributed across the different age groups? In more statistical language, can they be modelled by a uniform distribution? You could take a sample of accidents and find the ages of the drivers involved. You would not expect the frequencies in the age groups to be exactly the same, but how near would they have to be before you could say that they are uniformly distributed? After doing this chapter you will be able to conduct such investigations.

4.1 You need to be able to form hypotheses.

Goodness of fit is concerned with measuring how well an observed frequency distribution fits to a known distribution.

Suppose you take a die and throw it 120 times. You might get results like these:

Number, n	1	2	3	4	5	6
Observed frequency	23	15	25	18	21	18

If the die is *unbiased* you would, in theory, expect each of the numbers 1 to 6 to appear the same number of times.

For 120 throws the expected frequencies would each be

$P(X = x) \times 120 = \frac{1}{6} \times 120 = 20.$

You would expect results like these:

The expected results fit a uniform probability distribution:

x:	1	2	3	4	5	6
$P(X = x)$:	$\frac{1}{6}$	$\frac{1}{6}$	$\frac{1}{6}$	$\frac{1}{6}$	$\frac{1}{6}$	$\frac{1}{6}$

Number, n	1	2	3	4	5	6
Expected frequency	20	20	20	20	20	20

Since you are taking a sample, you should not be surprised that the observed frequency for each number doesn't exactly match the expected frequency.

However, suppose now the die was *biased*, you would not expect the observed frequency of each number to be exactly 20.

Although both the results from the biased and unbiased dice would differ from the predicted results, the results from the unbiased die should be better modelled by the discrete uniform distribution than are those from a biased die.

We form the **hypothesis** that the *observed frequency distribution does not differ from a theoretical one*, and that any differences are due to natural variations. Because this assumes no difference it is called the **null hypothesis**.

The **alternative hypothesis** is that the observed frequency distribution *does differ from the theoretical one* and that any differences are due to not only natural variations but the bias of the die as well.

H$_0$: there is *no difference* between the observed and the theoretical distribution.

H$_1$: there *is a difference* between the observed and the theoretical distribution.

In order to tell *how closely* the model fits the observed results you need to have a measure of the **goodness of fit** between the observed frequencies and the expected frequencies.

4.2 You need to be able to use goodness of fit.

This measure used for goodness of fit may best be understood by looking at an example.

Taking the results of the experiment with a die, you have:

Number on die, n	1	2	3	4	5	6
Observed frequency, O_i	23	15	25	18	21	18
Expected frequency, E_i	20	20	20	20	20	20

You can show this as a bar chart:

The thing you instinctively look at is the difference between the observed and the expected values.

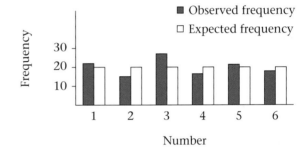

As a measure of the size of these differences we take the sum of the squares of the differences, divided by the expectation.

i.e. $\quad \sum \dfrac{(O_i - E_i)^2}{E_i}$ where

O_i = an observed frequency

E_i = an expected (theoretical) frequency, asserted by the null hypothesis.

This gives a positive number that gets larger as the differences between the observed and the expected frequencies get larger, and smaller as the differences get smaller.

- **The measure of goodness of fit is**

$$X^2 = \sum_{i=1}^{n} \dfrac{(O_i - E_i)^2}{E_i}$$

The symbol X^2 is used rather than just X because it shows that the value is never going to be negative.

You can see that the less good the fit, the larger the difference between each observed and expected value, and the greater the value of X^2.

Here is another way of calculating X^2.

$$X^2 = \sum \dfrac{(O_i - E_i)^2}{E_i} = \sum \dfrac{O_i^2 - 2O_iE_i + E_i^2}{E_i}$$

Multiply out the bracket.

$$= \sum \dfrac{O_i^2}{E_i} - \sum \dfrac{2O_iE_i}{E_i} + \sum \dfrac{E_i^2}{E_i}$$

$$= \sum \dfrac{O_i^2}{E_i} - \sum 2O_i + \sum E_i$$

Divide by E.

$$= \sum \dfrac{O_i^2}{E_i} - \sum O_i$$

Since $\sum E = \sum O$.

$$= \sum \dfrac{O_i^2}{E_i} - N$$

Since $\sum O = N$ (the number in the sample). (Note: This formula is not given in the formulae booklet, but is easier to use.)

4.3 You need to understand degrees of freedom.

In general degrees of freedom are calculated from the size of the sample. They are a measure of the amount of information from the sample data that has not been used up. Every time a statistic is calculated from a sample, one degree of freedom is used up.

In this chapter, in order to create a model for the observed frequency distribution, you must use the information about the data they contain in order to select a suitable model. To begin with you have n observed frequencies, and your model has to have the same total frequency as the observed distribution. The requirement that the totals have to agree is called a **constraint**, or **restriction**, and uses up one of your degrees of freedom.

In the Example in Section 4.2, with 120 tosses of the die, the expected and observed frequencies both have to add up to 120. The last frequency is decided by the values of the other frequencies. If the first five values are 20 the last value must also be 20 in order to make the totals agree. In our example of the die there are six expected frequencies, but only five that may be set independently. In this example you have one constraint so there are $6 - 1 = 5$ degrees of freedom.

The number of constraints will also depend on the number of parameters needed to describe the distribution and whether or not these parameters are known. If you do not know a parameter you have to estimate it from the observed data and this uses up a further degree of freedom.

Note: If the estimate of a parameter is *calculated* then it *is* a restriction. If it is guessed by using an estimate that seems sensible from observations then it it *not* a restriction.

It is usual to refer to each rectangle of a table that contains a piece of data as a cell. You sometimes have to combine frequencies from different cells of the table (the reason for this is given in the next section.) If cells are combined in this way then there are fewer expected values, so when you calculate the number of degrees of freedom you have to count the number of cells after any such combination and subtract the number of constraints from this.

■ **The number of degrees of freedom = number of cells (after any combining) − number of constraints.**

4.4 You need to be able to use the chi-squared (χ^2) family of distributions.

The χ^2 (pronounced kye-squared) family of distributions can be used as approximations for the statistic X^2. We write this

$$\bullet \quad X^2 = \sum \frac{(O_i - E_i)^2}{E_i} = \sum \frac{O_i^2}{E_i} - N \sim \chi^2$$

X^2 is approximated well by χ^2 *as long as none of the expected values* (E_i) *fall below* 5. If the expected values are less than 5 then you have to combine frequencies in the data table until the frequency is greater than 5. Usually frequencies adjacent to each other in the table are joined together because if one value is low the next one is also likely to be low as well. (This may be seen in Examples 2 and 3.)

The χ^2 family of distributions are theoretical ones. The probability distribution function of each member of the family is characterised by a parameter ν (nu), (which takes integer values), and the constant k_ν whose value depends on ν.

To distinguish which member of the family of distributions you are talking about you write χ^2_ν. Thus χ^2_4 is the χ^2 distribution with $\nu = 4$.

When selecting which of the χ^2 family to use as an approximation for X^2 you select the distribution which has ν **equal to the number of degrees of freedom** of your expected values.

4.5 You need to be able to test your hypotheses.

You began this chapter by forming a hypothesis that there was no difference between the observed and the theoretical distributions.

Next, you found a measure of goodness of fit. The question which arises is, 'could the value of $\sum \dfrac{(O_i - E_i)^2}{E_i}$ calculated for your sample come from a population for which $\sum \dfrac{(O_i - E_i)^2}{E_i}$ is equal to zero?'

As in book S2, you will only reject the null hypothesis if, by accepting the alternative hypothesis, you have only a small chance of being wrong. Typically this figure is set at 5%.

To find the value of $\sum \dfrac{(O_i - E_i)^2}{E_i}$ that is only exceeded with probability of 5% (the critical value), we use the appropriate χ^2 distribution.

For a given value of ν, the critical value of χ^2 which is exceeded with probability 5% is written $\chi^2_\nu (5\%)$ or $\chi^2_\nu (0.05)$.

> The table on page 137 gives you, for each value of ν, critical values of χ^2_ν for probabilities of 99.5%, 99%, 97.5%, 95%, and 90% (0.995, 0.99, 0.975, 0.95 and 0.9), and 10%, 5%, 2.5%, 1% and 0.5%.

Example 1

With $\nu = 5$ find the value of χ^2 that is exceeded with 0.05 probability.

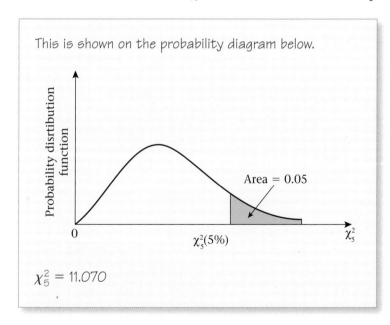

This is shown on the probability diagram below.

Area = 0.05

$\chi^2_5 (5\%)$

χ^2_5

$\chi^2_5 = 11.070$

> Look down the left of the table to get row $\nu = 5$.

> Look across the table to get column 0.050.

> Read off where row and column cross: the value is 11.070.

Also from the table, $\chi^2_5 (10\%) = 9.236$, $\chi^2_5 (2.5\%) = 12.832$, $\chi^2_5 (1\%) = 15.086$ and $\chi^2_5 (0.5\%) = 16.750$. For each other value of ν the critical values may be looked up in the same way.

Remember X^2 is approximated well by χ^2 so long as *none of the expected values (E_i) fall below 5*.

Let's go back to the die problem.

Example 2

In an experiment with tossing a die 120 times the frequency distribution is to be compared to a discrete uniform distribution as shown:

Number on die, n	1	2	3	4	5	6
Observed frequency, O_i	23	15	25	18	21	18
Expected frequency, E_i	20	20	20	20	20	20

Test, at the 5% significance level, whether or not the observed frequencies could be modelled by a discrete uniform distribution.

H_0: The observed distribution can be modelled by a discrete uniform distribution (the die is not biased).

H_1: The observed distribution cannot be modelled by a discrete uniform distribution (the die is biased).

The number of degrees of freedom is $6 - 1 = 5$

From the table on page 137 the critical value of χ^2 is 11.070 at the 5% level $\left(\chi^2_5 (5\%) = 11.070\right)$. i.e. $\chi^2_5 (5\%) = 11.070$

In this case you can calculate $\sum \dfrac{(O_i - E_i)^2}{E_i}$ as follows:

Number	1	2	3	4	5	6	Total
O_i	23	15	25	18	21	18	120
E_i	20	20	20	20	20	20	120
$\dfrac{(O_i - E_i)^2}{E_i}$	0.45	1.25	1.25	0.2	0.05	0.2	3.4
$\sum \dfrac{O_i^2}{E_i}$	26.45	11.25	31.25	16.20	22.05	16.20	123.4

$$\sum \frac{(O_i - E_i)^2}{E_i} = 3.4 \text{ OR } \sum \frac{O_i^2}{E_i} - N = 123.4 - 120 = 3.4$$

Since $3.4 < 11.070$ you do not reject the null hypothesis at the 0.05 level.

There is no evidence that the die is biased.

Write down your two hypotheses. (This time we are considering a particular distribution as a model, so we name the distribution in the hypothesis.)

Find the degrees of freedom.

Find the critical value.

Calculate $\sum \dfrac{(O_i - E_i)^2}{E_i}$ or $\sum \dfrac{O_i^2}{E_i} - N$

See if $\sum \dfrac{(O_i - E_i)^2}{E_i} <$ critical value.

Draw a conclusion based on the context.

Exercise 4A

1 An octagonal die is thrown 500 times and the results are noted. It is assumed that the die is unbiased. A test is to be done to see whether the observed results differ from the expected ones. Write down a null hypothesis and an alternative hypothesis that can be used.

2 For 5 degrees of freedom find the critical value of χ^2 which is exceeded with a probability of 5%.

3 Find the values of the following from the table on page 137.

    a χ_5^2 (5%)   **b** χ_8^2 (1%)   **c** χ_{10}^2 (10%)

4 With $\nu = 10$ find the value of χ^2 that is exceeded with 0.05 probability.

5 With $\nu = 8$ find the value of χ^2 that is exceeded with 0.10 probability.

6 The random variable Y has a χ^2 distribution with 8 degrees of freedom. Find y such that $P(Y < y) = 0.99$.

7 The random variable X has a χ^2 distribution with 5 degrees of freedom. Find x such that $P(X < x) = 0.95$.

8 The random variable Y has a χ^2 distribution with 12 degrees of freedom. Find:

    a y such that $P(Y < y) = 0.05$,   **b** y such that $P(Y < y) = 0.95$.

4.6 You need to know the general method for testing the goodness of fit.

1 Determine which distribution is likely to be a good model by examining the conditions applying to the observed data (the necessary conditions were given in Book S2).

2 Set the significance level, for example, 5%.   •————————   These will often be given in the question.

3 Estimate parameters (if necessary) from your observed data.

4 Form your hypotheses.

5 Calculate expected frequencies.

6 Combine any expected frequencies so that none are less than 5.

7 Find ν using ν = number of cells after combining − number of constraints or restrictions.

8 Find the critical value of χ^2 from the table.

9 Calculate $\displaystyle\sum \frac{(O_i - E_i)^2}{E_i}$ or $\displaystyle\sum \frac{O_i^2}{E_i} - N$.

10 See if your value is significant.

11 Draw the appropriate conclusion and interpret in the context of the original problem.

4.7 You need to be able to apply goodness-of-fit tests to discrete data.

You met three discrete distributions in book S2. The conditions under which each distribution arises, and the methods used in their calculation are repeated here for easy reference. You will also see how to use them as models for observed distributions.

Testing a discrete uniform distribution as a model

You have already seen an example of this. The conditions under which a discrete distribution arises are:

- the discrete random variable X is defined over a set of k distinct values,
- each value is equally likely.

The probability of each value is given by

$$P(X = x_r) = \frac{1}{k}, r = 1, 2, ..., k$$

The frequencies for a sample size of N are given by

$$\text{Frequency} = P(X = x_r) \times N = \frac{1}{k} \times N = \text{for } r = 1, 2, ..., k$$

Since we are using a uniform distribution there are no parameters to estimate and the only restriction is that the expected frequencies add up to N, the degrees of freedom ν = number of cells − 1.

Example 3

100 digits between 0 and 9 are selected from a table with the frequencies as shown below.

Digit	0	1	2	3	4	5	6	7	8	9
Frequency	11	8	8	7	8	9	12	9	13	15

Could the digits be from a random number table? Test at the 0.05 level.

Each digit should have an equal chance of selection, so the appropriate model is the discrete uniform distribution. —— Determine the distribution. The significance level is given as 5% and no parameters need estimating.

H_0: A discrete uniform distribution is a suitable model. (The digits are random.) —— State your hypotheses.

H_1: A discrete uniform distribution is not a suitable model. (The digits are not random.)

$$P(X = x_r) = \tfrac{1}{10} \quad r = 0, 1, ..., 9$$ —— Calculate estimated frequencies. No frequencies are less than 5.

The number of degrees of freedom is:

$$\nu = 10 - 1 = 9$$ —— Find ν.

From the table on page 137 χ^2_9 (5%) = 16.919 •——— Find the critical value.

Digit	0	1	2	3	4	5	6	7	8	9
Observed, O_i	11	8	8	7	8	9	12	9	13	15
Expected, E_i	10	10	10	10	10	10	10	10	10	10
$\dfrac{(O_i - E_i)^2}{E_i}$	0.1	0.4	0.4	0.9	0.4	0.1	0.4	0.1	0.9	2.5

$$\sum \frac{(O_i - E_i)^2}{E_i} = 6.2$$ •——————— Calculate $\sum \dfrac{(O_i - E_i)^2}{E_i}$ or $\sum \dfrac{O_i^2}{E_i} - N$.

So: $$\sum \frac{(O_i - E_i)^2}{E_i} < 16.919$$ •——————— See if your value is significant.

You do not reject H_0; there is no evidence to •——— suggest the digits are not random.

Draw a conclusion in the context of the original problem.

Testing a binomial distribution as a model

The conditions under which a binomial distribution arises are:

- there must be a fixed number (n) of trials in each observation,
- the trials must be independent,
- the trials have only two outcomes: success and failure,
- the probability of success (p) is constant.

For a binomial

$$P(X = x_r) = \binom{n}{r} p^r (1 - p)^{n-r} \qquad r = 0, 1, 2, \ldots, n$$

The frequency f_r with which each r occurs when the number of observations is N is given by

$$f_r = P(X = r) \times N$$

The binomial distribution has two parameters, n and p. You have the usual restriction that the expected frequencies have to have the same total as observed frequencies, while p may be known or it may be estimated from the observed values, by using frequencies of success.

$$p = \frac{\text{total number of successes}}{\text{number of trials} \times N} = \frac{\sum(r \times f_r)}{n \times N}$$

If p is not estimated by calculation: $\qquad \nu = \text{number of cells} - 1$

If p is estimated by calculation: $\qquad \nu = \text{number of cells} - 2$

Example **4**

The data in the table are thought to be modelled by a binomial B(10, 0.2). Use the table for the binomial cumulative distribution function to find expected values, and conduct a test to see if this is a good model. Use a 5% significance level.

x	0	1	2	3	4	5	6	7	8
Frequency of x	12	28	28	17	7	4	2	2	0

State your hypotheses.

H_O: A B(10, 0.2) distribution is a suitable model for the results.

H_1: The results cannot be modelled by a B(10, 0.2) distribution.

Calculate the frequencies. (From the table of the binomial cumulative distribution function (the table on page 131) you get the probabilities, and by multiplying by 100 (sum of observed frequencies) you get the expected frequencies.)

x	0	1	2	3
Probability of x	0.1074	0.2684	0.3020	0.2013
Expected frequencies	10.74	26.84	30.2	20.13

x	4	5	6	7	8
Probability of x	0.0881	0.0264	0.0055	0.0008	0.0001
Expected frequencies	8.81	2.64	0.55	0.08	0.01

There are $7 + 4 + 2 + 2 = 15$ observed values when $x \geqslant 4$

$P(x \geqslant 4) = 8.81 + 2.64 + 0.55 + 0.08 + 0.01 = 12.09$

Combine any expected frequencies < 5. (You will have to combine the last five cells in the table since $2.64 + 0.55 + 0.08 + 0.01 < 5$.)

O_i	12	28	28	17	15
E_i	10.74	26.84	30.20	20.13	12.09
$\dfrac{(O_i - E_i)^2}{E_i}$	0.1478	0.0501	0.1603	0.4867	0.7004

The number of degrees of freedom = number of cells after combining $- 1 = 5 - 1 = 4$ [p was not estimated by calculation this time].

Find the number of degrees of freedom.

Find the critical value.

From the table on page 137 the critical value x_4^2 (5%) is 9.488.

Calculate $\sum \dfrac{(O_i - E_i)^2}{E_i}$ or $\sum \dfrac{O_i^2}{E_i} - N$

$$\sum \frac{(O_i - E_i)^2}{E_i} = 1.5453$$

$1.545 < 9.488$

See if the value is significant.

You do not reject H_O: B (10, 0.2) is a possible model for these data.

Draw a conclusion.

Example 5

A study of the number of girls in families with five children was done on 100 such families. The results are summarised in the following table.

Number of girls (r)	0	1	2	3	4	5
Frequency (f)		13	18	38	20	10	1

It is suggested that the distribution may be modelled by a binomial distribution with $p = 0.5$.

a Give reasons why this might be so.

b Test, at the 5% significance level, whether or not a binomial distribution is a good model.

a There is a fixed number of children in the family so $n = 5$. The trials are independent (assume no multiple births). There are two outcomes to each trial: success (a girl), failure (a boy). The assumption that a girl is as likely as a boy is reasonable.

Compare the conditions with the known conditions for a binomial distribution.

b H_0: B(5, 0.5) is a suitable model.

H_1: B(5, 0.5) is not a suitable model.

State your hypotheses. Note that the value of p is given in the hypotheses.

r	0	1	2	3	4	5
O	13	18	38	20	10	1
E	3.12	15.63	31.25	31.25	15.63	3.12

Calculate the expected frequencies.

(The expected data can be calculated using the tables.)

Since 3.12 < 5 you must combine cells.

r	0 or 1	2	3	4 or 5
O	31	38	20	11
E	18.75	31.25	31.25	18.75

Combine cells so that no $E_i < 5$.

$$\sum \frac{(O_i - E_i)^2}{E_i} = 16.714$$

Calculate $\sum \frac{(O_i - E_i)^2}{E_i}$.

You have $4 - 1 = 3$ degrees of freedom.

Find the degrees of freedom.

From the tables: $\chi^2_3 (0.5) = 7.815$

$16.714 > 7.815$

Find the critical value. See if the result is significant.

You reject H_0: the number of girls in families of 5 children cannot be modelled by B(5, 0.5)

Draw a conclusion based on the context.

Example 6

Take the data from Example 5 and test it to see if a binomial distribution is a suitable model.

H_0: A binomial distribution is a suitable model

H_1: A binomial distribution is not a suitable model.

State your hypotheses.

The number of observations $N = 100$, the number of trials $n = 5$.

$$p = \frac{\sum(r \times f_r)}{100n} = \frac{199}{100 \times 5} = 0.398$$

Estimate p.

and, because you estimated p, there will be two constraints.

r	$P(r)$	E_i
0	$(0.602)^5 = 0.0791$	7.91
1	$5(0.602)^4(0.398) = 0.2614$	26.14
2	$10(0.602)^3(0.398)^2 = 0.3456$	34.56
3	$10(0.602)(0.398)^4 = 0.2285$	22.85
4	$5(0.602)^1(0.398)4 = 0.0755$	7.55
5	$(0.398)^5 = 0.0099$	0.99

Calculate the expected frequencies. (Because $p = 0.398$ you cannot use the tables and must use the formula instead.)

r	O_i	E_i	$\dfrac{O_i^2}{E_i}$
0	13	7.91	21.37
1	18	26.14	12.39
2	38	34.56	41.78
3	20	22.85	17.51
>3	11	8.54	14.17
Total			107.22

Combine cells if $E_i < 5$.

Calculate the degrees of freedom.

Find the critical value.

There are $5 - 2 = 3$ degrees of freedom.

The critical value is $\chi_3^2 = 7.815$.

Calculate $\sum\dfrac{(O_i)^2}{E_i} - N$ or $\sum\dfrac{(O_i - E_i)^2}{E_i}$.

$$\sum\frac{(O_i)^2}{E_i} - N = 107.22 - 100 = 7.22$$

$$7.22 < 7.815$$

See if your value is significant.

You do not reject H_0. A binomial is a suitable model.

Draw a conclusion.

Examples 5 and 6 are an example of how a model can be refined so that it is suitable.

Testing a Poisson distribution as a model

The conditions under which a Poisson distribution is likely to arise are:

- the N events occur *independently* of each other,
- the events occur *singly* and at random in continuous space or time,
- the events occur at a *constant rate*, in the sense that the mean number in an interval is proportional to the length of the interval,
- the mean and the variance are *equal*.

For a Poisson distribution with mean λ

$$P(X = r) = \frac{e^{-\lambda} \lambda^r}{r!} \qquad r = 0, 1, 2, \dots$$

Although, theoretically, r has an infinite number of integer values, in practice all those greater than or equal to some number n are put together and the probability $P(X \geq n)$ is found from:

$$P(X \geq n) = 1 - P(X < n)$$

You choose n equal to the highest value of r for which the observed frequency is > 0. In Example 7, n is chosen to be 7 since all telephone calls for $r \geq 8$ have zero frequencies.

The frequency f_r with which each r occurs is given by $P(X = r) \times N$.

The Poisson distribution has a single parameter λ, which may be known or which may be estimated from the observed data using;

$$\lambda = \frac{\sum(r \times f_r)}{N}.$$

There is the usual restriction on the total of the expected frequencies being equal to the total of the observed frequencies.

If λ is not estimated by calculation: $\nu = $ number of cells $- 1$
If λ is estimated by calculation: $\nu = $ number of cells $- 2$

Example 7

The numbers of telephone calls arriving at an exchange in six-minute periods were recorded over a period of 8 hours, with the following results.

Number of calls, r	0	1	2	3	4	5	6	7	8
Frequency, f_r	8	19	26	13	7	5	1	1	0

Can these results be modelled by a Poisson distribution? Test at the 5% significance level.

H_0: A Poisson distribution Po(λ) is a suitable model.

H_1: The calls cannot be modelled by a Poisson distribution.

Total number of observations $= N = \dfrac{8 \times 60}{6} = 80$

$\lambda = \dfrac{\sum(r \times f_r)}{N} = \dfrac{176}{80} = 2.2$

A particular Poisson distribution is not specified in the question.

Since you do not know the value of λ you must estimate it from the observed frequencies.

r	$P(X = r)$	Expected frequency of r
0	$\dfrac{e^{-2.2} \times 2.2^0}{1} = 0.1108$	8.864 (0.1108 × 80)
1	$\dfrac{e^{-2.2} \times 2.2^1}{1} = 0.2438$	19.504
2	$\dfrac{e^{-2.2} \times 2.2^2}{2} = 0.2681$	21.448
3	$\dfrac{e^{-2.2} \times 2.2^3}{3 \times 2} = 0.1966$	15.728
4	$\dfrac{e^{-2.2} \times 2.2^4}{4 \times 3 \times 2} = 0.1082$	8.656
5	$\dfrac{e^{-2.2} \times 2.2^5}{5 \times 4 \times 3 \times 2} = 0.0476$	3.808
6	$\dfrac{e^{-2.2} \times 2.2^6}{6 \times 5 \times 4 \times 3 \times 2} = 0.0174$	1.392
7 or more	$1 - 0.9925 = 0.0075$	0.6

$\lambda = 2.2$ is not in the table so you must calculate the expected frequencies.

The value for P($r = 7$ or more) is obtained by subtracting the sum of the other probabilities from 1.

r	O_i	E_i	$\dfrac{(O_i - E_i)^2}{E_i}$
0	8	8.864	0.0842
1	19	19.504	0.0130
2	26	21.448	0.9661
3	13	15.728	0.4732
4	7	8.656	0.3168
5 or more	7	5.8	0.2483

In this case you have to combine cells to give expected frequencies of more than 5.

$$\sum \frac{(O_i - E_i)^2}{E_i} = 2.1016$$

You have $6 - 2 = 4$ degrees of freedom,

From the table on page 137 χ_4^2 (5%) = 9.488

$2.1016 < 9.488$

So you have no evidence to reject H_o.

The calls may be modelled by a Po(2.2) distribution.

Since λ was estimated from the observed frequencies there are 2 constraints.

See if your value is significant.

Draw a conclusion.

Exercise 4B

1 The following table shows observed values for what is thought to be a discrete uniform distribution.

x	1	2	3	4	5	6	7	8
Frequency of x	12	24	18	20	25	17	21	23

a Calculate the expected frequencies and, using a 5% significance level, conduct a goodness of fit test.

b State your conclusions.

2 The following tables show observed values (O) and expected values (E) for a goodness of fit test of a binomial distribution model. The probability used in calculating the expected values has not been found from the observed values.

O	17	28	32	15	5	3
E	19.69	34.74	27.59	12.98	4.01	0.99

a Conduct the test using a 5% significance level and state your conclusions.

b Suggest how the model might be improved.

3 The following table shows observed values for a distribution which it is thought may be modelled by a Poisson distribution.

x	0	1	2	3	4	5	>5
Frequency of x	12	23	24	24	12	5	0

A possible model is thought to be Po(2). From tables, the expected values are found to be as shown in the following table.

x	0	1	2	3	4	5	>5
Expected frequency of x	13.53	27.07	27.07	18.04	9.02	3.61	1.66

a Conduct a goodness of fit test at the 5% significance level.

b It is suggested that the model could be improved by estimating the value of λ from the observed results. What effect would this have on the number of constraints placed upon the degrees of freedom?

4 A mail order firm receives packets every day through the mail.

They think that their deliveries are uniformly distributed throughout the week. Test this assertion, given that their deliveries over a 4-week period were as follows. Use a 0.05 significance level.

Day	Mon	Tues	Wed	Thurs	Fri	Sat
Frequency	15	23	19	20	14	11

5 Over a period of 50 weeks the number of road accidents reported to a police station were as shown.

Number of accidents	0	1	2	3	4
Number of weeks	15	13	9	13	0

  a Find the mean number of accidents per week.

  b Using this mean and a 0.10 significance level, test the assertion that these data are from a population with a Poisson distribution.

6 A marksman fires 6 shots at a target and records the number r of bull's-eyes hit. After a series of 100 such trials he analyses his scores, the frequencies being as follows.

r	0	1	2	3	4	5	6
Frequency	0	26	36	20	10	6	2

  a Estimate the probability of hitting a bull's-eye.

  b Use a test at the 0.05 significance level to see if these results are consistent with the assumption of a binomial distribution.

7 The table below shows the number of employees in thousands at five factories and the number of accidents in 3 years.

Factory	A	B	C	D	E
Employees (thousands)	4	3	5	1	2
Accidents	22	14	25	8	12

Using a 0.05 significance level, test the hypothesis that the number of accidents per 1000 employees is constant at each factory.

8 In a test to determine the red blood cell count in a patient's blood sample, the number of cells in each of 80 squares is counted with the following results.

Number of cells per square, x	0	1	2	3	4	5	6	7	8
Frequency, f	2	8	15	18	14	13	7	3	0

It is assumed that these will fit a Poisson distribution. Test this assertion at the 0.05 significance level.

9 A factory has a machine. The number of times it broke down each week was recorded over 100 weeks with the following results.

Number of times broken down	0	1	2	3	4	5
Frequency	50	24	12	9	5	0

It is thought that the distribution is Poisson.

  a Give reasons why this assumption might be made.

  b Conduct a test at the 0.05 level of significance to see if the assumption is reasonable.

10 In a lottery there are 505 prizes, and it is assumed that they will be uniformly distributed throughout the numbered tickets. An investigation gave the following:

Ticket number	1–1000	1001–2000	2001–3000	3001–4000	4001–5000	5001–6000	6001–7000	7001–8000	8001–9000	9001–10000
Frequency	56	49	35	47	63	58	44	52	51	50

Using a suitable test with a 0.05 significance level, and stating your null and alternative hypotheses, see if the assumption is reasonable.

11 Data were collected on the number of female puppies born in 200 litters of size 8. It was decided to test whether or not a binomial model with parameters $n = 8$ and $p = 0.5$ is a suitable model for these data. The following table shows the observed frequencies and the expected frequencies, to 2 decimal places, obtained in order to carry out this test.

Number of females	Observed number of litters	Expected number of litters
0	1	0.78
1	9	6.25
2	27	21.88
3	46	R
4	49	S
5	35	T
6	26	21.88
7	5	6.25
8	2	0.78

a Find the values of R, S and T.

b Carry out the test to determine whether or not this binomial model is a suitable one. State your hypotheses clearly and use a 5% level of significance.

An alternative test might have involved estimating p rather than assuming $p = 0.5$.

c Explain how this would have affected the test.

12 A random sample of 300 football matches was taken and the number of goals scored in each match was recorded. The results are given in the table below.

Number of goals	0	1	2	3	4	5	6	7
Frequency	33	55	80	56	56	11	5	4

a Show that an unbiased estimate of the mean number of goals scored in a football match is 2.4 and find an unbiased estimate of the variance.

It is thought that a Poisson distribution might provide a good model for the number of goals per match.

b State briefly an implication of a Poisson model on goal scoring at football matches.

Using a Poisson distribution, with mean 2.4, expected frequencies were calculated as follows:

Number of goals	0	1	2	3	4	5	6	7
Expected frequency	s	65.3	t	62.7	37.6	18.1	7.2	2.5

c Find the values of s and t.

d State clearly the hypotheses required to test whether or not a Poisson distribution provides a suitable model for these data.

In order to carry out this test the class for 7 goals is redefined as 7 or more goals.

e Find the expected frequency for this class.

The test statistic for the test in part **d** is 15.7 and the number of degrees of freedom used is 5.

f Explain fully why there are 5 degrees of freedom.

g Stating clearly the critical value used, carry out the test in part **d**, using a 5% level of significance.

13 A student of botany believed that *multifolium uniflorum* plants grow in random positions in grassy meadowland. He recorded the number of plants in one square metre of grassy meadow, and repeated the procedure to obtain the 148 results in the table.

Number of plants	0	1	2	3	4	5	6	7 or greater
Frequency	9	24	43	34	21	15	2	0

a Show that, to two decimal places, the mean number of plants in one square metre is 2.59.

b Give a reason why the Poisson distribution might be an appropriate model for these data.

Using the Poisson model with mean 2.59, expected frequencies corresponding to the given frequencies were calculated, to two decimal places, and are shown in the table below.

Number of plants	0	1	2	3	4	5	6	7 or greater
Expected frequencies	11.10	28.76	s	32.15	20.82	10.78	4.65	t

c Find the values of s and t to two decimal places.

d Stating clearly your hypotheses, test at the 5% level of significance whether or not this Poisson model is supported by these data.

4.8 You need to be able to apply goodness-of-fit tests to continuous distributions.

When dealing with continuous data you have to group the values into classes and then observe the frequency for each class.

Testing a normal distribution as a model

Some indicators which show that a normal distribution might be expected are:

- the distribution is 'bell shaped' and is symmetrical about the mean,
- approximately two-thirds of the values fall within one standard deviation of the mean.

The normal distribution has two parameters, μ and σ, which are either known or will have to be estimated from the observations.

The best estimates for μ and σ^2 are $\bar{x}$ and s^2.

$$\bar{x} = \frac{\sum x_i}{n} \text{ and } s^2 = \frac{\sum(x_i - \bar{x})^2}{n - 1} \text{ or } s^2 = \sum\frac{x_i^2}{n} - \bar{x}^2$$

where n is the total number of observations. (If the individual values of x are not known you use the mean value of the group in which they fall.)

If the parameters are not estimated:

$$\nu = \text{number of cells after combining} - 1$$

If both the parameters are estimated:

$$\nu = \text{number of cells after combining} - 3$$

If one parameter only is estimated:

$$\nu = \text{number of cells after combining} - 2$$

Because the normal distribution is continuous you can only conduct the test if your observations are collected together in class intervals, and you look at the frequency of occurrence within each class interval. If X is a variable then you will wish to know, for each class, the $P(a \leqslant X < b)$ where a and b are the real class boundaries. The normal distribution stretches from $-\infty$ to $+\infty$ so the end groups will be of the form $X < b$ at the bottom and $X > a$ at the top, when calculating probabilities.

You obtain the probabilities from the normal distribution table of $N(0, 1^2)$ using:

$$P(a < X < b) = P\left(\frac{a - \mu}{\sigma} < Z < \frac{b - \mu}{\sigma}\right)$$

$$= \Phi\left(\frac{b - \mu}{\sigma}\right) - \Phi\left(\frac{a - \mu}{\sigma}\right)$$

This was explained in book Sl.

The class frequencies are obtained by multiplying the probabilities by n.

Example 8

During observations on the height of 200 male students the following data were observed.

Height (cm)	150–154	155–159	160–164	165–169	170–174	175–179	180–184	185–189	190–194
Frequency	4	6	12	30	64	52	18	10	4

a Test at the 0.05 level to see if the height of male students could be modelled by a normal distribution with mean 172 and standard deviation 6.

b Describe how you would modify this test if the mean and variance were unknown.

a H_0: The normal distribution N(172, 36) is a suitable model.

     H_1: The normal distribution N(172, 36) is not a suitable model.

> State your hypotheses.

Classes a b	$\dfrac{b - \mu}{\sigma}$	$P(a \leqslant X < b)$ $= \Phi\left(\dfrac{b - \mu}{\sigma}\right) - \Phi\left(\dfrac{a - \mu}{\sigma}\right)$	Frequencies $P(a \leqslant X < b) \times n$
< 154.5	−2.92	0.0019 − 0.0000 = 0.0019	0.38
154.5–159.5	−2.08	0.0188 − 0.0019 = 0.0169	3.38
159.5–164.5	−1.25	0.1056 − 0.0188 = 0.0868	17.36
164.5–169.5	−0.42	0.3372 − 0.1056 = 0.2316	46.32
169.5–174.5	0.42	0.6628 − 0.3372 = 0.3256	65.12
174.5–179.5	1.25	0.8944 − 0.6628 = 0.2316	46.32
179.5–184.5	2.08	0.9812 − 0.8944 = 0.0869	17.36
184.5–189.5	2.92	0.9981 − 0.9812 = 0.0169	3.38
> 189.5		1.0000 − 0.9981 = 0.0019	0.38

Class	O_i	E_i	$\dfrac{(O_i - E_i)^2}{E_i}$
150–164	22	21.12	0.0367
165–169	30	46.32	5.7501
170–174	64	65.12	0.0193
175–179	52	46.32	0.6965
180–194	32	21.12	5.6048

> Before calculating the expected frequencies by using $f_r = P(a \leqslant X < b) \times n$ with $n = 200$, you must find the true class boundaries and convert these to Z values using $\mu = 172$ and $\sigma = 6$.

> You must combine frequencies less than 5.

Since μ and σ are not estimated:

The number of degrees of freedom = 5 − 1 = 4

From the tables the critical values $\chi_4^2 (0.05) = 9.488$

$$\sum \frac{(O_i - E_i)^2}{E_i} = 12.1074$$

> Calculate $\sum \dfrac{(O_i - E_i)^2}{E_i}$. You could have used the formula $\sum \dfrac{(O_i)^2}{E_i} - N$ instead.

$$\sum \frac{(O_i - E_i)^2}{E_i} > 9.488$$

> See if your value is significant.

You reject H_0: the normal distribution N(172, 36) is not a suitable model.

> Draw a conclusion.

The expected values in this example have been calculated using the normal table without interpolation. Some calculators will give this reading directly. If you use the figures given by a calculator they will be with interpolation and may differ slightly from those above. In your examination you can use the nearest value to z in the table but you will not be penalised if you do use interpolation.

b You would estimate the parameters as follows.

$$\bar{x} = \frac{152 \times 4 + 157 \times 6 + 162 \times 12 + 167 \times 30 + 172 \times 64 + 177 \times 52 + 182 \times 18 + 187 \times 10 + 192 \times 4}{200}$$

$$= 173.15$$

$$s^2 = [(152 - 173.15)^2 \times 4 + (157 - 173.15)^2 \times 6 + (162 - 173.15)^2 \times 12$$
$$+ (167 - 173.15)^2 \times 30 + (172 - 173.15)^2 \times 64 + (177 - 173.15)^2 \times 52$$
$$+ (182 - 173.15)^2 \times 18 + (187 - 173.15)^2 \times 10 + (192 - 173.15)^2 \times 4]$$
$$\div 199$$

$$= 58.22$$

$$s = 7.63$$

The test would be conducted with $5 - 3 = 2$ degrees of freedom.

Testing a continuous uniform distribution as a model

The indicators that show that a continuous uniform distribution might be expected are:

- symmetry about the mean,
- classes of equal width have equal probabilities.

A random variable X having a continuous uniform distribution over the interval (α, β) has a probability distribution function

$$f(x) = \begin{cases} \dfrac{1}{\beta - \alpha}, & \alpha < x < \beta, \\ 0, & \text{otherwise.} \end{cases}$$

Because of the continuous nature of the distribution you must collect your observations into n non-overlapping classes. You therefore will be looking at probabilities such as $P(a < X < b)$ where $a \geqslant \alpha$ and $b \leqslant \beta$. The probabilities may be calculated using

$$P(a < X < b) = \frac{b - a}{\beta - \alpha}$$

The continuous uniform distribution only has the requirement that the expected frequencies must equal the observed frequencies. Thus ν = number of cells $- 1$.

Example 9

In a study on the habits of a flock of starlings, the direction in which they headed when they left their roost in the mornings was recorded over 240 days. The direction was found by recording if they headed between certain features of the landscape. The compass bearings of these features were then measured. The results are given below.

Direction (degrees)	$0 \leqslant d < 58$	$58 \leqslant d < 100$	$100 \leqslant d < 127$	$127 \leqslant d < 190$	$190 \leqslant d < 256$	$256 \leqslant d < 296$	$296 \leqslant d < 360$
Frequency	31	40	47	40	32	30	20

It is suggested that they feed equally in all directions.

a Suggest a suitable model.

b Test to see if these data support this view.

a A suitable model would be the continuous uniform distribution because you would expect the distribution to be symmetrical about the mean and classes of equal width would be expected to have equal probabilities.

b H_0: The continuous uniform distribution is a suitable model (the starlings feed in all directions).

H_1: It is not a suitable model (they do not feed in all directions).

Class a to b	$b - a$	$P(a < x < b)$ $= \dfrac{b - a}{360 - 0}$	Frequency $= P(a \leqslant X < b) \times n$ $= P(a \leqslant X < b) \times 240$
$0 \leqslant d$ < 58	58	0.1611	38.67
$58 \leqslant d$ < 100	42	0.1167	28
$100 \leqslant d$ < 127	27	0.075	18
$127 \leqslant d$ < 190	63	0.175	42
$190 \leqslant d$ < 256	66	0.1833	44
$256 \leqslant d$ < 296	40	0.1111	26.66
$296 \leqslant d$ < 360	64	0.1778	42.67

Calculate the frequencies

There are $7 - 1 = 6$ degrees of freedom.

No parameter has been calculated so the only restriction is the usual one.

From the table $\chi^2_6(0.05) = 12.592$ •————————— Find the critical value.

Class	O_i	E_i	$\dfrac{(O_i - E_i)^2}{E_i}$
$0 \leqslant d < 58$	31	38.67	1.5213
$58 \leqslant d < 100$	40	28	5.1429
$100 \leqslant d < 127$	47	18	46.7222
$127 \leqslant d < 190$	40	42	0.0952
$190 \leqslant d < 256$	32	44	3.2727
$256 \leqslant d < 296$	30	26.66	0.4184
$296 \leqslant d < 360$	20	42.67	12.0443

$$\sum \frac{(O_i - E_i)^2}{E_i} = 69.2171$$ •———————

Calculate $\sum \dfrac{(O_i - E_i)^2}{E_i}$

or $\sum \dfrac{(O_i)^2}{E_i} - N.$

$$\sum \frac{(O_i - E_i)^2}{E_i} > 12.592$$ •———————

See if it is significant.

You reject H_0 and accept H_1. The continuous uniform distribution is *not* a suitable model. The birds do not feed •——— Draw your conclusion.
in all directions. They have preferred feeding areas.

It is clear that in this case the class 100–127 alone gives a significant result, so there is no need to carry on past this point. It also appears that the class 100–127 is more popular than the other classes. You have already discovered something about the birds' habits and you can count this a success. You might, however, like to consider how you would refine this model or what further investigations you could make. What is there about the feeding ground in this direction? What has this direction got in common with the other popular feeding areas? If this sector and its attractions is removed, do the birds feed equally in all directions? Does the direction in which they fly out truly represent their feeding ground?

Exercise 4C

1 The diameters of a random sample of 30 mass-produced components were measured by checking their diameter with gauges. Of the 30, 18 passed through a 4.0 mm gauge and of these 6 failed to pass through a 3.5 mm gauge. Test the hypothesis that the diameters of the components were a sample of a normal population with mean 3.8 mm and standard deviation 0.5 mm. Use a 5% significance level for your test.

2 An egg producer takes a sample of 150 eggs from his flock of chickens and grades them into classes according to their weights as follows.

Class	2	3	4	5	6
Weight	66–70	61–65	56–60	51–55	46–50
Frequency	10	32	67	29	12

Does this distribution fit a normal distribution of mean 58 g and standard deviation 4 g? Use a 5% significance level for your test.

3 A sample of 100 apples is taken from a load. The apples have the following distribution of sizes.

Diameter (cm)	$\leqslant 6$	7	8	9	$\geqslant 10$
Frequency	8	29	38	16	9

It is thought that they come from a normal distribution with mean diameter of 8 cm and a standard deviation of 0.9 cm. Test this assertion using a 0.05 level of significance.

4 A shop owner found that the number of cans of a particular drink sold per day during 100 days in summer was as follows.

Drinks per day, d	0 –	10 –	20 –	30 –	40–50
Frequency of d	10	24	45	14	7

It is thought that these data can be modelled by a normal distribution.

a Estimate values of μ and σ and conduct a goodness of fit test using 1% significance level.

b Explain how the shopkeeper might use this model.

5 An outfitter sells boys' raincoats and these are stocked in four sizes.

Size 1 fits boys up to 1.25 m in height. Size 2 fits boys from 1.26 to 1.31 m. Size 3 fits boys from 1.32 to 1.37 m. Size 4 fits those over 1.38 m. To assist the outfitter in deciding the stock levels he should order each year, the heights of 120 boys in the right age range were measured with the following results.

Height, $h(m)$	1.20–1.22	1.23–1.25	1.26–1.28	1.29–1.31
Frequency of h	9	9	18	23

Height, $h(m)$	1.32–1.34	1.35–1.37	1.38–1.40	1.41–1.43
Frequency of h	20	19	17	5

It is suggested that a suitable model for these data is N(1.32, 0.0016).

a Conduct a goodness of fit test using a $2\frac{1}{2}$% significance level.

b Estimate values of μ and σ using the observed values and using these conduct a goodness of fit test using a $2\frac{1}{2}$% significance level.

c Select the best model and use it to tell the outfitter how many of each size should be ordered per year if the normal annual sales are 1200.

6 A hamster breeder is studying the weight of adult hamsters. Each hamster from a random sample of 50 hamsters is weighed and the results, given to the nearest g, are recorded in the following table.

Weight (g)	85–94	95–99	100–104	105–109	110–119
Frequency	6	9	17	14	4

a Show that an estimate of the mean weight of the hamsters is 102 g.

The breeder proposes that the weight of an adult hamster, in g, should be modelled by the random variable W having a normal distribution with standard deviation 6. The breeder fits a normal distribution and obtains the following expected frequencies.

W	$W \leqslant 94.5$	$94.5 < W \leqslant 99.5$	$99.5 < W \leqslant 104.5$	$104.5 < W \leqslant 109.5$	$W > 109.5$
Expected frequency	r	11.64	s	11.64	t

b Find the values of r, s and t.

c Stating your hypotheses clearly, test at the 10% level of significance whether or not a normal distribution with a standard deviation of 6 is a suitable model for W.

4.9 You need to be able to use contingency tables.

So far in this chapter you have been concerned with the frequency with which a single event occurs. For example, you might count the number of times each of the numbers 1 to 6 appears when a die is thrown 100 times. The thing looked at in this case is the frequencies with which the numbers 1 to 6 appear. Sometimes you are interested in the frequencies with which two criteria are fulfilled at the same time. If you study the frequency with which A-Level Maths passes at grades A, B and C occur you may also be interested in which of two schools the students attended. Here you have two criteria: the pass level and the school. You can show these results by means of a contingency table, which shows the frequency with which each of the results occurred at each school separately.

		Pass (criterion 1)			
		A	B	C	Totals
School (criterion 2)	X	18	12	20	50
	Y	26	12	32	70
Totals		44	24	52	120

18 pupils at school X got a grade A pass.

32 pupils at school Y got a grade C pass.

A total of 44 pupils out of a total of 120 got a grade A pass.

This is called a **2 × 3** contingency table since there are two rows and three columns.

Setting the hypotheses

The thing we are interested in is whether there is any association between the two schools' sets of results. We pose the hypothesis 'are the two criteria independent?'.

H_0: School and grade of pass are independent.

H_1: School and grade of pass are not independent.

Selecting a model

If the hypothesis H_0 is true then you would expect school A to get $\frac{50}{120}$ of each grade and School B to get $\frac{70}{120}$ of each grade.

Now, overall: $P(A \text{ grade}) = \frac{44}{120}$

$P(\text{school } X) = \frac{50}{120}$

So

$$P(A \text{ grade and school } X) = P(A \text{ grade}) \times P(\text{school } X) = \frac{44}{120} \times \frac{50}{120}$$

The expected frequency of passes at A from school X is therefore

$$\frac{44}{120} \times \frac{50}{120} \times 120 = \frac{44 \times 50}{120} = 18.33$$

Notice that

- **expected frequency** $= \dfrac{\textbf{row total} \times \textbf{column total}}{\textbf{grand total}}$

The expected frequency is calculated on the assumption that the criteria are independent. You can find the other expected frequencies in the same way.

The expected frequencies are shown in the table.

		Pass (criterion 1)			
		A	**B**	**C**	**Totals**
School (criterion 2)	**X**	$\frac{50 \times 44}{120} = 18.33$	$\frac{50 \times 24}{120} = 10$	$\frac{50 \times 52}{120} = 21.67$	50
	Y	$\frac{70 \times 44}{120} = 25.67$	$\frac{70 \times 24}{120} = 14$	$\frac{70 \times 52}{120} = 30.33$	70
Totals		44	24	52	120

Degrees of freedom

When calculating expected values you need not calculate the last value in each row because the sum of the values in each row has to equal the row total.

This creates one constraint on the number of degrees of freedom.

For example, $P(C \text{ grade and school } X) = 50 - (18.33 + 10)$.

In the same way the last value in each of the other rows is fixed by the row total once the other value in the row is known.

This creates another constraint on the number of degrees of freedom.

For example: $P(A \text{ grade and school } Y) = 44 - 18.33$

In general, if there are h rows, then once $(h − 1)$ expected frequencies have been calculated the last value in the row is *fixed* by the row total. If there are k columns, once $(k − 1)$ columns have been calculated the last column value is fixed by the column total.

The number of independent variables is given therefore by $(h − 1)(k − 1)$. That is to say,

■ **The number of degrees of freedom = $v = (h − 1)(k − 1)$**

Example 10

Conduct a goodness of fit test, at the 5% significance level, on the data given for the two schools X and Y as given above.

H_0: School and grade of pass are independent.

You form your hypotheses.

H_1: School and grade of pass are not independent.

$v = (h − 1)(k − 1) = (2 − 1)(3 − 1) = 2$

Calculate the number of degrees of freedom.

From tables the critical value at the 0.05 significance level is 5.991.

Find the critical value.

O_i	E_i	$\dfrac{(O_i − E_i)^2}{E_i}$
18	18.33	0.0059
12	10.00	0.4000
20	21.67	0.1287
26	25.67	0.0042
12	14.00	0.2857
32	30.33	0.0920

The expected values have already been calculated on a previous page.

$$\sum \frac{(O_i − E_i)^2}{E_i} = 0.9165$$

Calculate $\sum \dfrac{(O_i − E_i)^2}{E_i}$

or $\sum \dfrac{O_i^2}{E_i} − N$.

So: $$\sum \frac{(O_i − E_i)^2}{E_i} < 5.991$$

See if the value is significant.

You do not reject H_0: there is insufficient evidence to suggest an association between the school and the grades of pass. School and grade of pass are independent.

Draw a conclusion.

Example 11

During the trial of a new drug, 60 volunteers out of 200 were treated with the drug. Those experiencing a relief of their symptoms and those who did not were recorded as follows:

	Relief	No relief	Totals
Treated	10	50	60
Not treated	40	100	140
Totals	50	150	200

Use a suitable test to see if there is any association between treatment with the drug and relief of symptoms. Use a 5% significance level.

H_0: Treatment and relief are independent (not associated).

H_1: Treatment and relief are not independent (associated).

Table of expected values:

	Relief	No relief
Treated	$\dfrac{60 \times 50}{200} = 15$	$\dfrac{60 \times 150}{200} = 45$
Not treated	$\dfrac{140 \times 50}{200} = 35$	$\dfrac{140 \times 150}{200} = 105$

Form your hypotheses.

Calculate the expected values.

$\nu = (2 - 1)(2 - 1) = 1$

Find the degrees of freedom.

From the table on page 137 the critical value χ_1^2 (5%) is 3.841.

O_i	E_i	$\dfrac{(O_i - E_i)^2}{E_i}$
10	15	1.6667
50	45	0.5556
40	35	0.7143
100	105	0.2381

$$\sum \frac{(O_i - E_i)^2}{E_i} = 3.1747$$

$$\sum \frac{(O_i - E_i)^2}{E_i} < 3.841$$

Calculate $\sum \dfrac{(O_i - E_i)^2}{E_i}$

or $\sum \dfrac{O_i^2}{E_i} - N$.

See if your value is significant.

So you do not reject H_0. There is no reason to believe there is an association between treatment and relief.

Draw a conclusion.

Exercise 4D

1 When analysing the results of a 3×2 contingency table it was found that

$$\sum_{i=1}^{6} \frac{(O_i - E_i)^2}{E_i} = 2.38$$

Write down the number of degrees of freedom and the critical value appropriate to these data in order to carry out a χ^2 test of significance at the 5% level. **E**

2 Three different types of locality were studied to see if the ownership, or non-ownership, of a television was or was not related to the locality. $\sum \dfrac{(O_i - E_i)^2}{E_i}$ was evaluated and found to be 13.1. Using a 5% level of significance, carry out a suitable test and state your conclusion.

3 In a college, three different groups of students sit the same examination. The results of the examination are classified as Credit, Pass or Fail. In order to test whether or not there is a difference between the groups with respect to the proportions of students in the three grades, the statistic $\sum \frac{(O_i - E_i)^2}{E_i}$ is evaluated and found to be equal to 10.28.

   a Explain why there are 4 degrees of freedom in this situation.

   b Using a 5% level of significance, carry out the test and state your conclusions.　　**E**

4 The grades of 200 students in both Mathematics and English were studied with the following results.

		English grades		
		A	B	C
Maths grades	A	17	28	18
	B	38	45	16
	C	12	12	14

Using a 0.05 significance level, test these results to see if there is an association between English and Mathematics results. State your conclusions.

5 The number of trains on time, and the number of trains that were late was observed at three different London stations. The results were:

		Observed frequency	
		On time	Late
Station	A	26	14
	B	30	10
	C	44	26

Using the χ^2 statistic and a significance test at the 5% level, decide if there is any association between station and lateness.

6 In addition to being classed into grades A, B, C, D and E, 200 students are classified as male or female and their results summarised in a contingency table. Assuming all expected values are 5 or more, the statistic $\sum \frac{(O_i - E_i)^2}{E_i}$ was 14.27.

Stating your hypotheses and using a 1% significance level, investigate whether or not gender and grade are associated.

7 In a random sample of 60 articles made in factory A, 13 were defective. In factory B, 12 out of 40 similar articles were defective.

   a Draw up a contingency table.

   b Test at the 0.05 significance level the hypothesis that quality was independent of the factory involved.

8 During an influenza epidemic, 15 boys and 8 girls became ill out of a year group of 22 boys and 28 girls. Assuming that this group may be treated as a random sample of the age group, test at the 5% significance level the hypothesis that there is no connection between gender and susceptibility to influenza.

9 In a study of marine organisms, a biologist collected specimens from three beaches and counted the number of males and females in each sample, with the following results;

		Beach		
		A	B	C
Gender	Male	46	80	40
	Female	54	120	160

Using a significance level of 5%, test these results to see if there is any difference between the beaches with regard to the numbers of male and female organisms.

10 A research worker studying the ages of adults and the number of credit cards they possess obtained the results shown below;

		Number of cards	
		≤ 3	≥ 3
Age	≤ 30	74	20
	≥ 30	50	35

Use the χ^2 statistic and a significance test at the 5% level to decide whether or not there is an association between age and number of credit cards possessed. **E**

Mixed exercise 4E

1 The random variable Y has a χ^2 distribution with 10 degrees of freedom. Find y such that $P(Y < y) = 0.99$. **E**

2 The random variable X has a chi-squared distribution with 8 degrees of freedom. Find x such that $P(X > x) = 0.05$.

3 As part of an investigation into visits to a Health Centre a 5×3 contingency table was constructed. A χ^2 test of significance at the 5% level is to be carried out on the table.

Write down the number of degrees of freedom and the critical region appropriate to this test. **E**

4 Data are collected in the form of a 4×4 contingency table.

To carry out a χ^2 test of significance one of the rows was amalgamated with another row and the resulting value of $\sum \dfrac{(O - E)^2}{E}$ calculated.

Write down the number of degrees of freedom and the critical value of χ^2 appropriate to this test assuming a 5% significance level. **E**

5 A new drug to treat the common cold was used with a randomly selected group of 100 volunteers. Each was given the drug and their health was monitored to see if they caught a cold. A randomly selected control group of 100 volunteers was treated with a dummy pill. The results are shown in the table below.

	Cold	No cold
Drug	34	66
Dummy pill	45	55

Using a 5% significant level, test whether or not the chance of catching a cold is affected by taking the new drug. State your hypotheses carefully. **E**

6 Breakdowns on a certain stretch of motorway were recorded each day for 80 consecutive days. The results are summarised in the table below.

Number of breakdowns	0	1	2	> 2
Frequency	38	32	10	0

It is suggested that the number of breakdowns per day can be modelled by a Poisson distribution.

Using a 5% significant level, test whether or not the Poisson distribution is a suitable model for these data. State your hypotheses clearly. **E**

7 A survey in a college was commissioned to investigate whether ot not there was any association between gender and passing a driving test. A group of 50 males and 50 females were asked whether they passed or failed their driving test at the first attempt. All the students asked had taken the test. The results were as follows.

	Pass	Fail
Male	23	27
Female	32	18

Stating your hypotheses clearly test, at the 10% level, whether or not there is any evidence of an association between gender and passing a driving test at the first attempt. **E**

8 Successful contestants in a TV game show were allowed to select from one of five boxes, four of which contained prizes, and one of which contained nothing. The boxes were numbered 1 to 5, and, when the show had run for 100 weeks, the choices made by the contestants were analysed with the following results:

Box number	1	2	3	4	5
Frequency	20	16	25	18	21

a Explain why these data could possibly be modelled by a discrete uniform distribution.

b Using a significance level of 5%, test to see if the discrete uniform distribution is a good model in this particular case.

9 A pesticide was tested by applying it in the form of a spray to 50 samples of 5 flies. The numbers of dead flies after 1 hour were then counted with the following results:

Number of dead flies	0	1	2	3	4	5
Frequency	1	1	5	11	24	8

a Calculate the probability that a fly dies when sprayed.

b Using a significance level of 5%, test to see if these data could be modelled by a binomial distribution.

10 The number of accidents per week at a certain road junction was monitored for four years. The results obtained are summarised in the table.

Number of accidents	0	1	2	> 2
Number of weeks	112	56	40	0

Using a 5% level of significance, carry out a χ^2 test of the hypothesis that the number of accidents per week has a Poisson distribution.   **E**

11 A tensile test is carried out on 100 steel bars which are uniform in section. The distances from the mid-points of the bars at which they fracture is recorded with the following results.

Distance	$0 < d \leqslant 10$	$10 < d \leqslant 20$	$20 < d \leqslant 30$	$30 < d \leqslant 40$	$40 < d \leqslant 50$	$50 < d \leqslant 60$
Frequency	15	17	18	20	12	18

Test at the 0.05 significance level if these data can be modelled by a continuous uniform distribution.

12 Samples of stones were taken at two points on a beach which were 1 mile apart. The rock types of the stones were found and classified as igneous, sedimentary or other types, with the following results.

		Site	
		A	B
Rock type	Igneous	30	10
	Sedimentary	55	35
	Other	15	15

Use a 5% significance level to see if the rocks at both sites come from the same population.

13 A small shop sells a particular item at a fairly steady yearly rate. When looking at the weekly sales it was found that the number sold varied. The results for the 50 weeks the shop was open were as shown in the table.

Weekly sales	0	1	2	3	4	5	6	7	8	> 8
Frequency	0	4	7	8	10	6	7	4	4	0

a Find the mean number of sales per week.

b Using a significance level of 5%, test to see if these can be modelled by a Poisson distribution.

14 A study was done of how many students in a college were left-handed and how many were right-handed. As well as left- or right-handedness the gender of each person was also recorded with the following results

	Left-handed	Right-handed
Male	100	600
Female	80	800

Use a significance test at the 0.05 level to see if there is an association between gender and left- and right-handedness.

Summary of key points

1 $\sum \dfrac{(O_i - E_i)^2}{E_i} - \chi^2$ OR $\sum \dfrac{O_i^2}{E_i} - N \sim \chi^2$

2 Degrees of freedom: ν = number of cells after combining − number of constraints.

3 If n is the number of cells after combining:

Distribution	Degrees of freedom	
	Parameters known	**Parameters not known**
Discrete uniform	$n - 1$	
Binomial	$n - 1$	$n - 2$
Poisson	$n - 1$	$n - 2$
Normal	$n - 1$	$n - 3$ (both unknown) $n - 2$ (one unknown)
Continuous uniform	$n - 1$	

4 For contingency tables:

$$\text{expected frequency} = \frac{\text{row total} \times \text{column total}}{\text{grand total}}$$

For an $h \times k$ table, degrees of freedom $\nu = (h - 1)(k - 1)$

After completing this chapter you should be able to:

- calculate Spearman's rank correlation coefficient
- calculate Spearman's rank correlation coefficient when there are no ties by using the easy formula
- test the hypothesis that a product moment correlation coefficient is zero
- test the hypothesis that Spearman's rank correlation coefficient is zero.

Regression and correlation

Cows at an agricultural show were ranked by an official judge. You ranked these cows prior to judging taking place. How does your ranking compare with that of the judge? Is there any agreement between the two sets of ranks? After doing this chapter you will be able to find out.

5.1 You need to know about Spearman's rank correlation coefficient.

In book S1 you used the product-moment correlation coefficient r as a measure of the strength of association between the paired observations (x_i, y_i), $i = 1, 2, ..., n$, where both x and y can be measured on a continuous scale. This is reasonable when you are dealing with measurable characteristics such as height or weight, etc. There are cases where it is not possible or may not be worthwhile to measure certain variables. For example, suppose a manufacturer of tea produced a number of different blends; you could taste each blend and place the blends in order of preference. You do not, however, have a numerical scale for measuring your preference. Similarly, it may be quicker to arrange a group of individuals in order of height than to measure each one. Under these circumstances, Spearman's rank correlation coefficient is used.

Spearman's rank correlation coefficient is denoted by r_s. In principle, r_s is simply a special case of the Pearson product-moment coefficient in which the data are converted to **rankings** before calculating the coefficient. It is also used when one, or both, variables is measured on an ordinal scale.

> Spearman's rank correlation coefficient is sometimes used as an approximation for the product-moment correlation coefficient as it is easier to calculate.

■ **To rank two sets of data X and Y, you give the rank 1 to the highest of the x_i values, 2 to the next highest, 3 to the next highest, and so on. You do the same for the y_i values.**

> It makes no difference if you rank the smallest as 1, the next smallest as 2, etc., provided you do the same to both X and Y.

Example 1

Two tea tasters were asked to rank nine blends of tea in their order of preference. The tea they liked best was ranked 1. Their orders of preference are shown in the table:

Blend	A	B	C	D	E	F	G	H	I
Taster 1 (x)	3	6	2	8	5	9	7	1	4
Taster 2 (y)	5	6	4	2	7	8	9	1	3

Calculate the Spearman rank correlation coefficient for these data.

x_i	y_i	x_i^2	y_i^2	$x_i y_i$	
3	5	9	25	15	
6	6	36	36	36	
2	4	4	16	8	
8	2	64	4	16	Find x_i^2, y_i^2, $x_i y_i$.
5	7	25	49	35	
9	8	81	64	72	
7	9	49	81	63	
1	1	1	1	1	
4	3	16	9	12	
$\sum x_i = 45$	$\sum y_i = 45$	$\sum x_i^2 = 285$	$\sum y_i^2 = 285$	$\sum x_i y_i = 258$	Find $\sum x_i$, $\sum y_i$, $\sum x_i^2$, $\sum y_i^2$ and $\sum x_i y_i$.

$$r_s = \frac{S_{xy}}{\sqrt{S_{xx}S_{yy}}} = \frac{\sum x_i y_i - \dfrac{\sum x_i \sum y_i}{n}}{\sqrt{\left[\left(\sum x_i^2 - \dfrac{(\sum x_i)^2}{n}\right)\left(\sum y_i^2 - \dfrac{(\sum y_i)^2}{n}\right)\right]}}$$

Use the standard formula to calculate r_s.

$$= \frac{258 - \dfrac{45 \times 45}{9}}{\sqrt{\left(285 - \dfrac{45 \times 45}{9}\right)\left(285 - \dfrac{45 \times 45}{9}\right)}}$$

$$= \frac{33}{\sqrt{(60 \times 60)}}$$

$$= 0.55$$

Spearman's rank correlation coefficient is derived from the product-moment correlation coefficient, so:

+1   means that rankings are in perfect agreement

−1   means that the rankings are in exact reverse order

0   means that there is no correlation between the rankings.

A quicker way of finding Spearman's rank correlation coefficient

In practice a simpler procedure is normally used to calculate r_s. The raw scores are converted to ranks, and the differences d between the ranks of each observation on the two variables are calculated.

If there are no tied ranks, then r_s is given by:

■ $r_s = 1 - \dfrac{6\sum d^2}{n(n^2 - 1)}$

where:
d_i = the difference between each rank of corresponding values of x and y, and
n = the number of pairs of values.

If there are tied ranks, the classic Pearson's correlation coefficient between ranks could be used instead of this formula. In practice, if there are only one or two tied ranks, the shorter formula gives a reasonable estimate for r_s.

Example 2

During a cattle show two judges ranked ten cattle for quality according to the following table.

Cattle	A	B	C	D	E	F	G	H	I	J
Judge A	1	5	2	6	4	8	3	7	10	9
Judge B	3	6	2	7	5	8	1	4	9	10

Find Spearman's rank correlation coefficient between the two judges and comment on the result.

A	B	d	d^2
1	3	−2	4
5	6	−1	1
2	2	0	0
6	7	−1	1
4	5	−1	1
8	8	0	0
3	1	2	4
7	4	3	9
10	9	1	1
9	10	−1	1
		Total	22

Find d^2 for each set of ranks.

Note that in an examination you do not need to show the table, but you should show the value of $\sum d^2$.

Find $\sum d^2$.

$$r_s = 1 - \frac{6 \times 22}{10(100 - 1)} = 0.867$$

Calculate r_s.

There is a reasonable degree of agreement between the two judges.

Draw a conclusion.

Example 3

The marks of eight pupils in French and German language tests were as follows.

Student	A	B	C	D	E	F	G	H
French, f(%)	52	25	86	33	55	57	54	46
German, g(%)	40	48	65	57	41	39	63	34

Calculate the product-moment correlation coefficient for f and g.

f	g	rank f	rank g	d	d^2
52	40	5	6	−1	1
25	48	8	4	4	16
86	65	1	1	0	0
33	57	7	3	4	16
55	41	3	5	−2	4
57	39	2	7	−5	25
54	63	4	2	2	4
46	34	6	8	−2	4
			Totals	0	70

The sum of the d's always comes to 0. This checks that you have not made a mistake.

$$\sum d^2 = 70$$

$$r_s = 1 - \frac{6\sum d^2}{n(n^2 - 1)}$$

$$= 1 - \frac{6 \times 70}{8(64 - 1)}$$

$$= 0.1666 \ldots$$

There is little agreement between the two subjects.

Many students make the mistake of using the formula as

$$r_s = \frac{1 - 6\sum d^2}{n(n^2 - 1)}$$

This loses marks in the examination.

When you use the same data the values of r and r_s do not come out the same. Because of the loss of detail in ranking, the value of r is in general more accurate as a measure of correlation than r_s.

The product-moment correlation coefficient and Spearman's rank correlation coefficient measure different things. Spearman's rank correlation coefficient does not make any assumptions about the frequency distribution of the variables, it does not require the assumption that the relationship between the variables is linear, nor does it require the variables to be measured on interval scales. Pearson's product-moment correlation coefficient requires both variables to be jointly normally distributed.

Exercise 5A

1 For each of the data sets of ranks given below, calculate the Spearman's rank correlation coefficient and interpret the result.

a

r_x	1	2	3	4	5	6
r_y	3	2	1	5	4	6

b

r_x	1	2	3	4	5	6	7	8	9	10
r_y	2	1	4	3	5	8	7	9	6	10

c

r_x	5	2	6	1	4	3	7	8
r_y	5	6	3	8	7	4	2	1

2 The number of goals scored by football teams and their positions in the league were recorded as follows for the top 12 teams.

Team	A	B	C	D	E	F	G	H	I	J	K	L
Goals	49	44	43	36	40	39	29	21	28	30	33	26
League position	1	2	3	4	5	6	7	8	9	10	11	12

a Find $\sum d^2$.

b Calculate Spearman's rank correlation coefficient for these data.
What conclusions can be drawn from this result?

3 A sample of a class's statistics projects was taken, and the projects were assessed by two teachers independently. Each teacher decided their rank order with the following results.

Project	A	B	C	D	E	F	G	H
Teacher A	5	8	1	6	2	7	3	4
Teacher B	7	4	3	1	6	8	2	5

a Find $\sum d^2$.

b Calculate the rank correlation coefficient and state any conclusions you draw from it.

4 A veterinary surgeon and a trainee veterinary surgeon both rank a small herd of cows for quality. Their rankings are shown below.

Cow	A	D	F	E	B	C	H	J
Qualified vet	1	2	3	4	5	6	7	8
Trainee vet	1	2	5	6	4	3	8	7

Find the rank correlation coefficient for these data, and comment on the experience of the trainee vet.

5 Two adjudicators at an ice dance skating competition award marks as follows.

Competitor	A	B	C	D	E	F	G	H	I	J
Judge 1	7.8	6.6	7.3	7.4	8.4	6.5	8.9	8.5	6.7	7.7
Judge 2	8.1	6.8	8.2	7.5	8.0	6.7	8.5	8.3	6.6	7.8

a Explain why you would use Spearman's rank correlation coefficient in this case.

b Calculate the rank correlation coefficient r_s, and comment on how well the judges agree.

6 **a** A teacher believes that he can predict the positions in which his students will finish in an A-Level examination. When the results were out he wished to compare his predictions with the actual results. Which correlation test should he use and why?

b The table shows predicted and actual orders.

Student	A	B	C	D	E	F	G	H	I	J
Predicted, p	2	4	1	3	8	6	9	5	10	7
Actual, a	3	4	2	8	1	6	7	9	10	5

Calculate Spearman's rank correlation coefficient r_s between a and p. Comment on the result.

7 A doctor assessed the lung damage suffered by a number of his patients who smoked, and asked each one 'For how many years have you smoked?' with the following results.

Patient	A	B	C	D	E	F	G
Number of years smoked	15	22	25	28	30	31	42
Lung damage grade	30	50	55	35	40	42	58

Calculate Spearman's rank correlation coefficient r_s and comment on the result. Give your value of $\sum d^2$.

5.2 You need to be able to test the hypothesis that a correlation coefficient is zero.

If a calculated value for a correlation coefficient is very near zero, you may be satisfied that no linear correlation exists. You say 'near zero' because your sets of data are samples from a population, and each time you take a sample you would get a different value of the product-moment correlation coefficient r. How near must the value be to zero before you can say there is zero correlation? The rest of this chapter is concerned with this problem. First look at the product-moment correlation coefficient.

Product-moment correlation coefficient

Suppose that:

1 the observed variables can be modelled by variables X and Y which are jointly normally distributed,

2 that X and Y have a correlation coefficient ρ (rho) and that r (the product-moment correlation coefficient) is an unbiased estimator of ρ.

Suppose X and Y have a population product-moment correlation coefficient $\rho = 0$. The diagram for the probability distribution function f(r) is symmetrical about $r = 0$ as shown below.

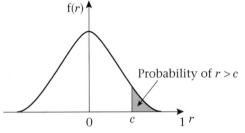

> As usual, the probability that r exceeds any given value c is given by the area under the graph to the right of c, and the probability of getting a value of r less than c is given by the area to the left of c.

As with all tests of significance you are interested in a value of c which r exceeds with a small probability. This is called the *critical value* of r. The table on page 138 gives critical values of r (one-tailed test) for different probability levels at different values of n (the number of pairs of readings).

Product-moment coefficient					
Level					Sample size
0.10	0.05	0.025	0.01	0.005	
0.8000	0.9000	0.9500	0.9800	0.9900	4
0.6870	0.8054	0.8783	0.9343	0.9587	5
0.6084	0.7293	0.8114	0.8822	0.9172	6
0.5509	0.6694	0.7545	0.8329	0.8745	7
0.5067	0.6215	0.7967	0.7887	0.8343	8
0.4716	0.5822	0.6664	0.7498	0.7977	9

> For a sample size of 8 you see from the table that the critical value of r to be significant at the 0.05 level on a one-tailed test is 0.6215.

You set up two hypotheses

The null hypothesis which is H_0: $\rho = 0$. (The population product-moment correlation coefficient = 0.)

The alternative hypothesis,

H_1: $\rho \neq 0$ ———————————————— This will be a two-tailed test.

OR

H_1: $\rho > 0$

OR

H_1: $\rho < 0$

These will be one-tailed tests.

Example 4

By using $\sum x = 20$, $\sum y = 35$, $\sum xy = 65$, $\sum x^2 = 35$, $\sum y^2 = 130$, calculate the product-moment correlation between 20 pairs of readings. Using a 0.05 significance level, test the hypothesis that $\rho = 0$ (use a two-tailed test).

H_0: $\rho = 0$ (there is zero correlation between the readings)

H_1: $\rho \neq 0$ (two-tailed) (there is either a positive or a negative correlation)

State your hypotheses.

Look at the question to see which of the alternative hypotheses to use.

$$r_s = \frac{S_{xy}}{\sqrt{S_{xx}S_{yy}}} = \frac{\sum x_i y_i - \frac{\sum x_i \sum y_i}{n}}{\sqrt{\left[\left(\sum x_i^2 - \frac{(\sum x_i)^2}{n}\right)\left(\sum y_i^2 - \frac{(\sum y_i)^2}{n}\right)\right]}}$$

Calculate r.

$$= \frac{65 - \frac{20 \times 35}{20}}{\sqrt{\left[\left(35 - \frac{20^2}{20}\right)\left(130 - \frac{35^2}{20}\right)\right]}}$$

$$= 0.934\ldots$$

From the table on page 138 the critical values of r are ± 0.4438 and the critical region is $r < -0.4438$ or $r > 0.4438$.

Find the critical value from the tables.

$0.934\ldots > 0.4438$.

The result is significant at the 0.05 level.

Test to see if the result is significant.

There is evidence to reject H_0 and accept H_1: there is evidence to suggest that the correlation is not zero.

Draw a conclusion.

Example 5

The product-moment correlation coefficient between 30 pairs of reactions is $r = -0.45$. Using a 0.05 significance level, test whether or not ρ differs from 0.

H_0: $\rho = 0$ (there is zero correlation between the readings)

H_1: $\rho \neq 0$ (two-tailed) (there is either a positive or a negative correlation)

State your hypotheses. Look at the question and decide which alternative hypothesis to use.

$r = -0.45$

Give the value of r.

From the table on page 138 the critical values of r are ± 0.3610 and the critical region is $r < -0.3610$ and $r > 0.3610$.

Find the critical values and region.

Since $-0.45 < -0.3610$ the value of r is significant at the 0.05 level.

Test the significance of r.

You reject H_0 and accept H_1: $\rho \neq 0$.
There is evidence of some correlation.

Draw a conclusion.

Example 6

For 8 pairs of observations the product-moment correlation coefficient is $r = 0.667$. Does this value indicate:

a a correlation significantly different to zero at the 5% level,

b a significant positive correlation at the 5% level?

a H_0: $\rho = 0$ (there is zero correlation between the readings)

H_1: $\rho \neq 0$ (two-tailed test) (there is either a positive or a negative correlation)

> State your hypotheses. Look to see which alternative hypothesis to use.

$r = 0.667$

> Find the value of r.

From the table on page 138 for a sample size of 8 the critical values are ± 0.7067.

The critical region is $r < -0.7067$ and $r > 0.7067$.

> Find the critical value.

Since $r = 0.667 > -0.7067$ and < 0.7067, it is not significant at the 5% level.

> Test the significance of r.

You do not reject H_0: $\rho = 0$. There is no evidence to show that the correlation is significantly different to zero.

> Draw a conclusion.

b H_0: $\rho = 0$ (there is zero correlation between the readings)

H_1: $\rho > 0$ (one-tailed test) (there is a positive correlation)

> State your new hypotheses.

$r = 0.667$

> Give a value for r.

From the table on page 138 for a sample size of 8 the critical value is 0.6215 and the critical region is $r > 0.6215$.

> Find the new critical value.

Since $r = 0.667 > 0.6215$ it is significant at the 5% level.

> Test the significance.

You reject H_0 and accept H_1: there is evidence of a positive correlation at the 5% level.

> Draw a conclusion.

Exercise 5B

1 A product-moment correlation coefficient of 0.3275 was obtained from a sample of 40 pairs of values. Test whether or not this value shows evidence of correlation:

a at the 0.05 level (use a two-tailed test), **b** at the 0.02 level (use a two-tailed test).

2 a Calculate the product-moment correlation coefficient for the following data, giving values for S_{xx}, S_{yy} and S_{xy}.

x	2	3	4	4	5	5	6
y	7	6	5	4	3	2	1

b Test, for these data, the null hypothesis that there is no correlation between x and y. Use a 1% significance level. State any assumptions you have made.

3 The ages X (years) and heights Y (cm) of 11 members of a football team were recorded and the following statistics were used to summarise the results.

$$\sum X = 168, \quad \sum Y = 1275, \quad \sum XY = 20\,704, \quad \sum X^2 = 2585 \quad \sum Y^2 = 320\,019$$

a Calculate the product-moment correlation coefficient for these data.

b Test the assertion that height and weight are positively correlated by using a suitable test. State your conclusion in words and any assumptions you have made. (Use a 5% level of significance.)

4 a Explain briefly your understanding of the term 'correlation'. Describe how you used, or could have used, correlation in a project or in class work.

b Twelve students sat two Biology tests, one theoretical the other practical. Their marks are shown below.

Marks in theoretical test (t)	5	9	7	11	20	4	6	17	12	10	15	16
Marks in practical test (p)	6	8	9	13	20	9	8	17	14	8	17	18

Find to 3 significant figures,

i the value of S_{tp} **ii** the product-moment correlation coefficient.

c Use a 0.05 significance level and a suitable test to check the statement that 'students who do well in theoretical Biology also do well in practical Biology tests'.

5 The following table shows the marks attained by 8 students in English and Mathematics tests.

Student	A	B	C	D	E	F	G	H
English	25	18	32	27	21	35	28	30
Mathematics	16	11	20	17	15	26	32	20

a Calculate the product-moment correlation coefficient.

A teacher thinks that the population correlation coefficient between the marks is likely to be zero.

b Test the teacher's idea at the 5% level of significance.

6 A small company decided to import fine Chinese porcelain. They believed that in the long term this would prove to be an increasingly profitable arrangement with profits increasing proportionally to sales. Over the next 6 years their sales and profits were as shown in the table below.

Year	1994	1995	1996	1997	1998	1999
Sales in thousands	165	165	170	178	178	175
Profits in £1000	65	72	75	76	80	83

Using a 1% significance level test to see if there is any evidence that the company's beliefs were correct, and that profit and sales were positively correlated.

5.3 You need to be able to test the hypothesis that Spearman's population rank correlation coefficient is zero.

Since Spearman's rank correlation coefficient was derived from the product-moment correlation coefficient, you might expect r_s to have a similar distribution when $\rho = 0$. The table on page 138 gives minimum critical values for r_s for different values of n from 4 upwards. A section of the table is shown below.

Sample size	Spearman's coefficient		
	Level		
	0.05	0.025	0.01
4	1.0000	–	–
5	0.9000	1.0000	1.0000
6	0.8286	0.8857	0.9429
7	0.7143	0.7857	0.8929
8	0.6429	0.7381	0.8333
9	0.6000	0.7000	0.7833

For a sample size of 8 you see from the table that the critical value of r_s to be significant at the 0.025 level on a one-tailed test is 0.7381.

As before, you start with a null hypothesis H_0: $\rho = 0$, and use as your alternative hypothesis:

H_1: $\rho \neq 0$ (two-tailed test),

or H_1: $\rho > 0$ (one-tailed test)

or H_1: $\rho < 0$ (one-tailed test).

Example 7

A rank correlation coefficient was found to be $r_s = 0.773$ from a ranking of $n = 6$. Is this significantly different from 0 at the 5% level?

H_0: $\rho = 0$ (the correlation is zero).

H_1: $\rho \neq 0$ (the correlation is either positive or negative).

$r_s = 0.773$

From the tables for a sample size of 6 at the 0.05 significance level the critical values are ± 0.8857.

(Note 0.025 in each tail.)

But $r_s = 0.773 > -0.8857$ and $r_s = 0.773 < 0.8857$, so the result is not significant at the 0.05 level.

You do not reject H_0. There is no evidence to suggest that $\rho \neq 0$.

State your hypotheses. Look at the question to decide which alternative hypothesis to use.
Give or calculate r_s.

Find the critical values from the table.

See if r_s is significant.

Draw a conclusion.

Example 8

The popularity of 16 subjects at a comprehensive school was found by counting the number of boys and the number of girls who chose each subject and then ranking the subjects. The results are shown in the table below.

Subject	A	B	C	D	E	F	G	H	I	J	K	L	M	N	O	P
Boys' ranks, b	2	5	9	8	1	3	15	16	6	10	12	14	4	7	11	13
Girls' ranks, g	4	7	11	3	6	9	12	16	5	13	10	8	2	1	15	14

Calculate Spearman's rank correlation coefficient and use a suitable test at the 1% level to investigate the statement, 'boys' and girls' choices are positively correlated'.

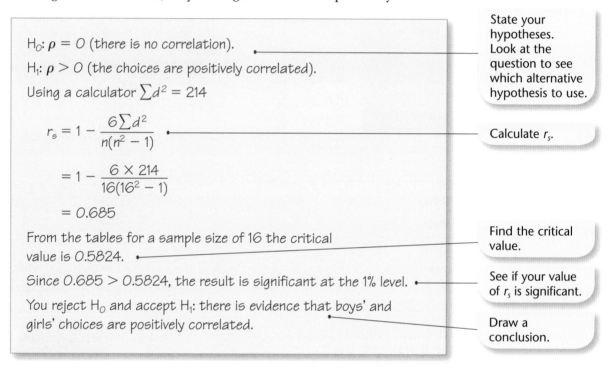

$H_0: \rho = 0$ (there is no correlation).

$H_1: \rho > 0$ (the choices are positively correlated).

State your hypotheses. Look at the question to see which alternative hypothesis to use.

Using a calculator $\sum d^2 = 214$

$r_s = 1 - \dfrac{6\sum d^2}{n(n^2 - 1)}$

Calculate r_s.

$= 1 - \dfrac{6 \times 214}{16(16^2 - 1)}$

$= 0.685$

From the tables for a sample size of 16 the critical value is 0.5824.

Find the critical value.

Since $0.685 > 0.5824$, the result is significant at the 1% level.

See if your value of r_s is significant.

You reject H_0 and accept H_1: there is evidence that boys' and girls' choices are positively correlated.

Draw a conclusion.

Exercise 5C

(Use a 5% significance level unless otherwise stated.)

1 A Spearman's rank correlation obtained from the fuel consumption of a selection of 30 cars and their engine sizes gave a rank correlation coefficient $r_s = 0.5321$. Investigate whether or not the fuel consumption is related to the engine size. State your null and alternative hypotheses. (Use a 5% level of significance.)

2 For one of the activities at a gymnastics competition, 8 gymnasts were awarded marks out of 10 for each of artistic performance and technical ability. The results were as follows.

Gymnast	A	B	C	D	E	F	G	H
Technical ability	8.5	8.6	9.5	7.5	6.8	9.1	9.4	9.2
Artistic performance	6.2	7.5	8.2	6.7	6.0	7.2	8.0	9.1

The value of the product-moment correlation coefficient for these data is 0.774.

a Stating your hypotheses clearly and using a 1% level of significance, test for evidence of a positive association between technical ability and artistic performance. Interpret this value.

b Calculate the value of the rank correlation coefficient for these data.

c Stating your hypotheses clearly and using a 1% level of significance, interpret this coefficient.

d Explain why the rank correlation coefficient might be the better one to use with these data. **E**

3 Two judges ranked 8 ice skaters in a competition according to the table below.

Judge \ Skater	i	ii	iii	iv	v	vi	vii	viii
A	2	5	3	7	8	1	4	6
B	3	2	6	5	7	4	1	8

a Evaluate Spearman's rank correlation coefficient between the ranks of the two judges.

b Use a suitable test, at the 5% level of significance. Interpret your findings to investigate for evidence of positive association between the rankings of the judges. **E**

4 Each of the teams in a school hockey league had the total number of goals scored by them and against them recorded, with the following results.

Team	A	B	C	D	E	F	G
Goals for	39	40	28	27	26	30	42
Goals against	22	28	27	42	24	38	23

Investigate whether there is any association between the goals for and those against by using Spearman's rank correlation coefficient. Use a suitable test at the 1% level to investigate the statement, 'A team that scores a lot of goals concedes very few goals'.

5 The weekly takings and weekly profits for six branch shops of a company are set out below.

Shop	1	2	3	4	5	6
Takings (£)	400	6200	3600	5100	5000	3800
Profits (£)	400	1100	450	750	800	500

a Calculate the coefficient of rank correlation, r_s, between the takings and profit.

b It is assumed that profits and takings will be positively correlated. Using a suitable hypothesis test (stating the null and alternative hypotheses) test this assertion at the 5% level of significance.

6 The rankings of 12 students in Mathematics and Music were as follows.

Mathematics	1	2	3	4	5	6	7	8	9	10	11	12
Music	6	4	2	3	1	7	5	9	10	8	11	12

a Calculate the coefficient of rank correlation r_s. [Show your value of $\sum d^2$.]

b Test the assertion that there is no correlation between these subjects. State the null and alternative hypotheses used. Use a 5% significance level.

7 a A child is asked to place 10 objects in order and gives the ordering

A   C   H   F   B   D   G   E   J   I

The correct ordering is

A   B   C   D   E   F   G   H   I   J

Find a coefficient of rank correlation between the child's ordering and the correct ordering.

b Use a 5% significance level and test whether there is an association between the child's order and the correct ordering. Draw conclusions about this result.   **E**

8 The crop of a root vegetable was measured over six consecutive years, the years being ranked for wetness. The results are given in the table below.

Year	1	2	3	4	5	6
Crop (10 000 tons)	62	73	52	77	63	61
Rank of wetness	5	4	1	6	3	2

Calculate, to 3 decimal places, a Spearman's rank correlation coefficient for these data. Test the assertion that crop and wetness are not correlated. (Use a 5% level of significance.)   **E**

Mixed exercise 5D

1 a Two judges at a cat show place the 10 entries in the following rank orders.

Cat	A	B	C	D	E	F	G	H	I	J
First judge	4	6	1	2	5	3	10	9	8	7
Second judge	2	9	3	1	7	4	6	8	5	10

Find a coefficient of rank correlation between the two rankings and, using the tables provided, comment on the extent of the agreement between the two judges.

b Explain briefly the role of the null and alternative hypotheses in a test of significance.   **E**

2 a Explain briefly the conditions under which you would measure association using a rank correlation coefficient.

b Nine applicants for places at a college were interviewed by two tutors. Each tutor ranked the applicants in order of merit. The rankings are shown below.

Applicant	A	B	C	D	E	F	G	H	I
Tutor 1	1	2	3	4	5	6	7	8	9
Tutor 2	1	3	5	4	2	7	9	8	6

Investigate the extent of the agreement between the two tutors.   **E**

3 In a ski-jump contest each competitor made two jumps. The order of merit for the 10 competitors who completed both jumps are shown.

Ski-jumper	A	B	C	D	E	F	G	H	I	J
First jump	2	9	7	4	10	8	6	5	1	3
Second jump	4	10	5	1	8	9	2	7	3	6

a Calculate, to 2 decimal places, a rank correlation coefficient for the performance of the ski-jumpers in the two jumps.

b Using a 5% significance, and quoting from the table of critical values, investigate whether there is a positive association between the two jumps. State your null and alternative hypotheses clearly. **E**

4 An expert on porcelain is asked to place seven china bowls in date order of manufacture, assigning the rank 1 to the oldest bowl. The actual dates of manufacture and the order given by the expert are shown below.

Bowl	A	B	C	D	E	F	G
Date of manufacture	1920	1857	1710	1896	1810	1690	1780
Order given by expert	7	3	4	6	2	1	5

a Find, to 3 decimal places, the Spearman's rank correlation coefficient between the order of manufacture and the order given by the expert.

b Refer to the table of critical values to comment on your results. State clearly the null hypothesis being tested. **E**

5 A small bus company provides a service for a small town and some neighbouring villages. In a study of their service a random sample of 20 journeys was taken and the distances x, in kilometres, and journey times t, in minutes, were recorded. The average distance was 4.535 km and the average journey time was 15.15 minutes.

a Using $\sum x^2 = 493.77$, $\sum t^2 = 4897$, $\sum xt = 1433.8$, calculate the product-moment correlation coefficient for these data.

b Stating your hypotheses clearly test, at the 5% level, whether or not there is evidence of a positive correlation between journey time and distance.

c State any assumptions that have to be made to justify the test in **b**. **E**

6 A group of students scored the following marks in their Statistics and Geography examinations.

Student	A	B	C	D	E	F	G	H
Statistics	64	71	49	38	72	55	54	68
Geography	55	50	51	47	65	45	39	82

a Find the value of the Spearman's rank correlation coefficient between the marks of these students.

b Stating your hypotheses and using a 5% level of significance, test whether marks in Statistics and marks in Geography are associated.

7 An international study of female literacy investigated whether there was any correlation between the life expectancy of females and the percentage of adult females who were literate. A random sample of 8 countries was taken and the following data were collected.

Life expectancy (years)	49	76	69	71	50	64	78	74
Literacy (%)	25	88	80	62	37	86	89	67

a Evaluate Spearman's rank correlation coefficient for these data.

b Stating your hypotheses clearly test, at the 5% level of significance, whether or not there is evidence of a correlation between the rankings of literacy and life expectancy for females.

c Give one reason why Spearman's rank correlation coefficient and not the product-moment correlation coefficient has been used in this case. **E**

8 Six friesian cows were ranked in order of merit at an agricultural show by the official judge and by a student vet.

The ranks were as follows:

Official judge	1	2	3	4	5	6
Student vet	1	5	4	2	6	3

a Calculate Spearman's rank correlation coefficient between these rankings.

b Investigate whether or not there was agreement between the rankings of the judge and the student.
State clearly your hypotheses, and carry out an appropriate one-tailed significance test at the 5% level. **E**

9 As part of a survey in a particular profession, age, x years, and salary, £y thousands, were recorded.

The values of x and y for a randomly selected sample of ten members of the profession are as follows:

x	30	52	38	48	56	44	41	25	32	27
y	22	38	40	34	35	32	28	27	29	41

a Calculate, to 3 decimal places, the product-moment correlation coefficient between age and salary.

b State two conditions under which it might be appropriate to use Spearman's rank correlation coefficient.

c Calculate, to 3 decimal places, the Spearman's rank correlation coefficient between age and salary.

It is suggested that there is no correlation between age and salary.

d Set up appropriate null and alternative hypotheses and carry out an appropriate test. (Use a 5% significance level.) **E**

10 A machine hire company kept records of the age, X months, and the maintenance costs, £Y, of one type of machine. The following table summarises the data for a random sample of 10 machines.

Machine	A	B	C	D	E	F	G	H	I	J
Age, x	63	12	34	81	51	14	45	74	24	89
Maintenance costs, y	111	25	41	181	64	21	51	145	43	241

a Calculate, to 3 decimal places, the product-moment correlation coefficient.
(You may use $\sum x^2 = 30\,625$, $\sum y^2 = 135\,481$, $\sum xy = 62\,412$.)

b Calculate, to 3 decimal places, the Spearman's rank correlation coefficient.

c For a different type of machine similar data were collected. From a large population of such machines a random sample of 10 was taken and the Spearman's rank correlation coefficient, based on $\sum d^2 = 36$, was 0.782.
Using a 5% level of significance and quoting from the tables of critical values, interpret this rank correlation coefficient. Use a two-tailed test and state clearly your null and alternative hypotheses. **E**

11 The data below show the height above sea level, x metres, and the temperature, y °C, at 7.00 a.m., on the same day in summer at nine places in Europe.

Height, x (m)	1400	400	280	790	390	590	540	1250	680
Temperature, y (°C)	6	15	18	10	16	14	13	7	13

a The product-moment correlation coefficient is -0.975. Test this for negative correlation at the 5% significance level. Interpret your result in context.

On the same day the number of hours of sunshine was recorded and Spearman's rank correlation between hours of sunshine and temperature, based on $\sum d^2 = 28$, was 0.767.

b Stating your hypotheses and using a 5% two-tailed test, interpret this rank correlation coefficient. **E**

12 a Explain briefly, referring to your project work if you wish, the conditions under which you would measure association by using a rank correlation coefficient rather than a product-moment coefficient.

b At an agricultural show 10 Shetland sheep were ranked by a qualified judge and by a trainee judge. Their rankings are shown in the table.

Qualified judge	1	2	3	4	5	6	7	8	9	10
Trainee judge	1	2	5	6	7	8	10	4	3	9

Calculate a rank correlation coefficient for these data.

c Using a suitable table and a 5% significance level, state your conclusions as to whether there is some degree of agreement between the two sets of ranks. **E**

13 a Explain briefly the use of a null hypothesis and a level of significance in statistical work.

b The positions in a league table of 8 rugby clubs at the end of a season are shown, together with the average attendance (in hundreds) at home matches during the season.

Club	A	B	C	D	E	F	G	H
Position	1	2	3	4	5	6	7	8
Average attendance	30	32	12	19	27	18	15	25

Calculate the coefficient of rank correlation between position in the league and home attendance. Comment on your results.

(E)

14 The ages, in months, and the weights, in kg, of a random sample of nine babies are shown in the table below.

Baby	A	B	C	D	E	F	G	H	I
Age (x)	1	2	2	3	3	3	4	4	5
Weight (y)	4.4	5.2	5.8	6.4	6.7	7.2	7.6	7.9	8.4

a The product-moment correlation coefficient between weight and age for these babies was found to be 0.972. By testing for positive correlation at the 5% significance level interpret this value.

b A boy who does not know the weights or ages of these babies is asked to list them, by guesswork, in order of increasing weight. He puts them in the order

$$A \quad C \quad E \quad B \quad G \quad D \quad I \quad F \quad H$$

Obtain, to 3 decimal places, a rank correlation coefficient between the boy's order and the true weight order.

c Referring to the tables and using a 5% significance level, investigate for any agreement between the boy's order and the weight order. Discuss any conclusions you draw from your results.

(E)

Summary of key points

1 To rank two sets of data X and Y, you give the rank 1 to the highest of the x_i values, 2 to the next highest, 3 to the next highest, and so on. You do the same for the y_i values.

2 Spearman's rank correlation coefficient is

$$r_s = \frac{S_{xy}}{\sqrt{S_{xx}S_{yy}}}$$

with ranks being used rather than values.

3 Spearman's rank correlation coefficient is given by

$$r_s = 1 - \frac{6\sum d^2}{n(n^2 - 1)} \qquad \text{where } d_i = (x_i - y_i).$$

Review Exercise

1 During a village show, two judges, *P* and *Q*, had to award a mark out of 30 to some flower displays. The marks they awarded to a random sample of 8 displays were as follows:

Display	A	B	C	D	E	F	G	H
Judge *P*	25	19	21	23	28	17	16	20
Judge *Q*	20	9	21	13	17	14	11	15

a Calculate Spearman's rank correlation coefficient for the marks awarded by the two judges.

After the show, one competitor complained about the judges. She claimed that there was no positive correlation between their marks.

b Stating your hypotheses clearly, test whether or not this sample provides support for the competitor's claim. Use a 5% level of significance.

2 The Director of Studies at a large college believed that students' grades in Mathematics were independent of their grades in English. She examined the results of a random group of candidates who had studied both subjects and she recorded the number of candidates in each of the 6 categories shown.

	Maths grade A or B	Maths grade C or D	Maths grade E or U
English grade A or B	25	25	10
English grade C to U	5	30	15

a Stating your hypotheses clearly, test the Director's belief using a 10% level of significance. You must show each step of your working.

The Head of English suggested that the Director was losing accuracy by combining the English grades C to U in one row. He suggested that the Director should split the English grades into two rows, grades C or D and grades E or U as for Mathematics.

b State why this might lead to problems in performing the test. **(E)**

3 A quality control manager regularly samples 20 items from a production line and records the number of defective items x. The results of 100 such samples are given in Table 1 below.

x	0	1	2	3	4	5	6	7 or more
Frequency	17	31	19	14	9	7	3	0

Table 1

a Estimate the proportion of defective items from the production line.

The manager claimed that the number of defective items in a sample of 20 can be modelled by a binomial distribution. He used the answer in part **a** to calculate the expected frequencies given in Table 2.

x	0	1	2	3	4	5	6	7 or more
Expected frequency	12.2	27.0	r	19.0	s	3.2	0.9	0.2

Table 2

b Find the value of r and the value of s giving your answers to 1 decimal place.

c Stating your hypotheses clearly, use a 5% level of significance to test the manager's claim.

d Explain what the analysis in part **c** tells the manager about the occurrence of defective items from this production line. **(E)**

4 The table below shows the price of an ice cream and the distance of the shop where it was purchased from a particular tourist attraction.

Shop	Distance from tourist attraction (m)	Price (£)
A	50	1.75
B	175	1.20
C	270	2.00
D	375	1.05
E	425	0.95
F	580	1.25
G	710	0.80
H	790	0.75
I	890	1.00
J	980	0.85

a Find, to 3 decimal places, the Spearman rank correlation coefficient between the distance of the shop from the tourist attraction and the price of an ice cream.

b Stating your hypotheses clearly and using a 5% one-tailed test, interpret your rank correlation coefficient. **(E)**

5 Five coins were tossed 100 times and the number of heads recorded. The results are shown in the table below.

Number of heads	0	1	2	3	4	5
Frequency	6	18	29	34	10	3

a Suggest a suitable distribution to model the number of heads when five unbiased coins are tossed.

b Test, at the 10% level of significance, whether or not the five coins are unbiased. State your hypotheses clearly. **E**

6 People over the age of 65 are offered an annual flu injection. A health official took a random sample from a list of patients who were over 65. She recorded their gender and whether or not the offer of an annual flu injection was accepted or rejected. The results are summarised below.

Gender	Accepted	Rejected
Male	170	110
Female	280	140

Using a 5% significance level, test whether or not there is an association between gender and acceptance or rejection of an annual flu injection. State your hypotheses clearly. **E**

7 An area of grass was sampled by placing a 1 m × 1 m square randomly in 100 places. The numbers of daisies in each of the squares were counted. It was decided that the resulting data could be modelled by a Poisson distribution with mean 2. The expected frequencies were calculated using the model.

The following table shows the observed and expected frequencies.

Number of daisies	Observed frequency	Expected frequency
0	8	13.53
1	32	27.07
2	27	r
3	18	s
4	10	9.02
5	3	3.61
6	1	1.20
7	0	0.34
$\geqslant 8$	1	t

a Find values for r, s and t.

b Using a 5% significance level, test whether or not this Poisson model is suitable. State your hypotheses clearly.

An alternative test might have been to estimate the population mean by using the data given.

c Explain how this would have affected the test. **E**

121

8 The numbers of deaths from pneumoconiosis and lung cancer in a developing country are given in the table.

Age group (years)	20–29	30–39	40–49	50–59	60–69	70 and over
Deaths from pneumoconiosis (1000s)	12.5	5.9	18.5	19.4	31.2	31.0
Deaths from lung cancer (1000s)	3.7	9.0	10.2	19.0	13.0	18.0

The correlation between the number of deaths in the different age groups for each disease is to be investigated.

a Give **one** reason why Spearman's rank correlation coefficient should be used.

b Calculate Spearman's rank correlation coefficient for these data.

c Use a suitable test, at the 5% significance level, to interpret your result. State your hypotheses clearly. **E**

9 Students in a mixed sixth form college are classified as taking courses in either arts, science or humanities. A random sample of students from the college gave the following results.

		Course		
		Arts	Science	Humanities
Gender	Boy	30	50	35
	Girl	40	20	42

Showing your working clearly, test, at the 1% level of significance, whether or not there is an association between gender and the type of course taken. State your hypotheses clearly. **E**

10 The product-moment correlation coefficient is denoted by r and Spearman's rank correlation coefficient is denoted by r_s.

a Sketch separate scatter diagrams, with five points on each diagram, to show

i $r = 1$,

ii $r_s = -1$ but $r > -1$.

Two judges rank seven collie dogs in a competition. The collie dogs are labelled A to G and the rankings are as follows.

Rank	1	2	3	4	5	6	7
Judge 1	A	C	D	B	E	F	G
Judge 2	A	B	D	C	E	G	F

b i Calculate Spearman's rank correlation coefficient for these data.

ii Stating your hypotheses clearly, test, at the 5% level of significance, whether or not the judges are generally in agreement. **E**

11 Ten cuttings were taken from each of 100 randomly selected garden plants. The number of cuttings that did not grow were recorded.

The results are as follows.

Number of cuttings which did not grow	0	1	2	3	4	5	6	7	8, 9 or 10
Frequency	11	21	30	20	12	3	2	1	0

a Show that the probability of a randomly selected cutting, from this sample, not growing is 0.223.

A gardener believes that a binomial distribution might provide a good model for the number of cuttings, out of 10, that do not grow.

He uses a binomial distribution, with the probability 0.2 of a cutting not growing. The calculated expected frequencies are as follows.

Number of cuttings which did not grow	0	1	2	3	4	5 or more
Expected frequency	r	26.84	s	20.13	8.81	t

b Find the values of r, s and t.

c State clearly the hypotheses required to test whether or not this binomial distribution is a suitable model for these data.

The test statistic for the test is 4.17 and the number of degrees of freedom used is 4.

d Explain fully why there are 4 degrees of freedom.

e Stating clearly the critical value used, carry out the test using a 5% level of significance.

12 A researcher carried out a survey of three treatments for a fruit tree disease.

	No action	Remove diseased branches	Spray with chemicals
Tree died within 1 year	10	5	6
Tree survived for 1–4 years	5	9	7
Tree survived beyond 4 years	5	6	7

Test, at the 5% level of significance, whether or not there is any association between the treatment of the trees and their survival. State your hypotheses and conclusion clearly.

13 Over a period of time, researchers took 10 blood samples from one patient with a blood disease. For each sample, they measured the levels of serum magnesium, s mg/dl, in the blood and the corresponding level of the disease protein, d mg/dl. The results are shown in the table.

s	1.2	1.9	3.2	3.9	2.5	4.5	5.7	4.0	1.1	5.9
d	3.8	7.0	11.0	12.0	9.0	12.0	13.5	12.2	2.0	13.9

[Use $\sum s^2 = 141.51$, $\sum d^2 = 1081.74$ and $\sum sd = 386.32$]

a Draw a scatter diagram to represent these data.

b State what is measured by the product-moment correlation coefficient.

c Calculate S_{ss}, S_{dd} and S_{sd}.

d Calculate the value of the product-moment correlation coefficient r between s and d.

e Stating your hypotheses clearly, test, at the 1% significance level, whether or not the correlation coefficient is greater than zero.

f With reference to your scatter diagram, comment on your result in part **e**.   **E**

14 The number of times per day a computer fails and has to be restarted is recorded for 200 days. The results are summarised in the table.

Number of restarts	Frequency
0	99
1	65
2	22
3	12
4	2

Test whether or not a Poisson model is suitable to represent the number of restarts per day. Use a 5% level of significance and state your hypothesis clearly.   **E**

15 A research worker studying colour preference and the age of a random sample of 50 children obtained the results shown below.

Age in years	Red	Blue	Totals
4	12	6	18
8	10	7	17
12	6	9	15
Totals	28	22	50

Using a 5% significance level, carry out a test to decide whether or not there is an association between age and colour preference. State your hypotheses clearly.   **E**

16 A manufacturer claims that the batteries used in his mobile phones have a mean lifetime of 360 hours and a standard deviation of 20 hours, when the phone is left on standby. To test this claim 100 phones were left on standby until the batteries ran flat. The lifetime t hours of the batteries was recorded.

The results are as follows.

t	300–	320–	340–	350–	360–	370–	380–	400–
Frequency	1	9	28	20	16	18	7	1

A researcher believes that a normal distribution might provide a good model for the lifetime of the batteries

She calculated the expected frequencies as follows using the distribution N ~ (360, 20).

t	< 320	320–	340–	350–	360–	370–	380–	400–
Expected frequency	2.28	13.59	24.26	r	s	14.98	13.59	2.28

a Find the values of r and s.

b Stating clearly your hypotheses, test, at the 1% level of significance, whether or not this normal distribution is a suitable model for these data.

Examination style paper

1 A class of primary school children consists of 32 girls. Each day 12 of the girls are brought to school by car and the others walk. The teacher wishes to estimate the average distance travelled to school each day by the class.

Explain briefly how the teacher could select a sample of 8 pupils using

a a systematic sample, (3)

b a stratified sample. (3)

2 The weights of men are normally distributed with a mean of 80 kg and a standard deviation of 10 kg.

The weights of women are normally distributed with a mean of 65 kg and a standard deviation of 5 kg. The weights of men and women are independent.

Find the probability that

a 6 randomly chosen men and 2 randomly chosen women will weigh more than 600 kg in total, (5)

b a randomly chosen male will weigh less than 1.5 times a randomly chosen female. (6)

3 A machine is known to dispense liquid into cartons such that the volume dispensed is normally distributed. It is claimed by the manufacturer of this machine that the mean volume dispensed is 100 ml.

In a series of trials on this machine the following values were recorded.

$$104.4 \quad 101.7 \quad 103.6 \quad 99.2 \quad 102.2$$
$$107.6 \quad 96.2 \quad 105.8 \quad 104.7 \quad 98.6$$

a Calculate unbiased estimates of the mean and the variance of the population of volumes dispensed by the machine. (5)

Given that the standard deviation of the volume of liquid dispensed is 3.4 ml,

b find a 95% confidence interval for the mean volume of liquid dispensed by this machine. (5)

c Use your interval to comment on the claim of the manufacturer. (1)

d Comment on the likely reaction of purchasers receiving cartons from the machine. (1)

4 The lifetime of 100 Globrite light bulbs selected at random had a mean value of 1400 hours with a standard deviation of 150 hours. The lifetime of 200 Luxiglo light bulbs selected at random had a mean lifetime of 1350 hours and a standard deviation of 140 hours.

a Stating your hypotheses clearly test, at the 1% level of significance, whether or not there is a difference between the mean lifetimes of these two types of bulb. (7)

b State the importance of the Central Limit Theorem in carrying out the test in part **a**. (1)

5 A survey of the number of hours spent watching television each week was carried out. The sample, randomly selected from a large population, contained 240 males and 200 females. The results are summarised below.

		Number of hours		
		Under 10 hours	10–25	Over 25 hours
Gender	Male	40.0%	47.5%	12.5%
	Female	32.5%	51.5%	16%

Stating your hypotheses clearly and using a 5% significance level, test whether or not there is an association between gender and time spent watching television. (11) **E**

6 The number of accidents per day on a stretch of motorway was recorded and the following results were obtained over a period of 100 days.

Number of accidents	0	1	2	3	4	$\geqslant 5$
Number of days	44	32	9	10	5	0

a Show that the mean number of accidents per day is 1. (2)

An accident investigator decided that the resulting data could be modelled by a Poisson distribution. Using a mean of 1 he calculated expected frequencies and the results are given below.

Number of accidents	0	1	2	3	4	$\geqslant 5$
Number of days	36.79	36.79	r	6.13	1.53	s

b Find the values of r and s. Give your answers to two decimal places. (3)

c Using a 1% level of significance, test whether or not this Poisson model is suitable. State your hypotheses clearly. (7)

7 A group of 10 children sat tests in Mathematics and Verbal Reasoning. Their results were as follows where x represents their Mathematics score and y their Verbal Reasoning score.

x	19	4	12	15	11	13	17	29	16	20
y	39	30	22	28	25	37	20	45	32	34

a Calculate Spearman's rank correlation coefficient for these data. (6)

b Stating your hypotheses clearly, test, at the 5% level of significance, whether or not there is a positive association between Mathematics and Verbal Reasoning scores. (5)

The product-moment correlation coefficient for these results is 0.583.

c Stating your hypotheses clearly test, at the 5% level of significance, whether or not the correlation coefficient is greater than zero. (3)

d State a reason why the conclusions of the two tests seem to conflict. (1)

Appendix

Statistics S3

Candidates sitting S3 may also require those formulae listed under Statistics S1 and S2.

Expectation algebra

For independent random variables X and Y

$$\mathrm{E}(XY) = \mathrm{E}(X)\,\mathrm{E}(Y)\,,\ \mathrm{Var}(aX \pm bY) = a^2\,\mathrm{Var}(X) + b^2\,\mathrm{Var}(Y)$$

Sampling distributions

For a random sample $X_1, X_2, \ldots, X_n$ of n independent observations from a distribution having mean μ and variance σ^2

$\overline{X}$ is an unbiased estimator of μ, with $\mathrm{Var}(\overline{X}) = \dfrac{\sigma^2}{n}$

S^2 is an unbiased estimator of σ^2, where $S^2 = \dfrac{\sum(X_i - \overline{X})^2}{n-1}$

For a random sample of n observations from $\mathrm{N}(\mu,\ \sigma^2)$

$$\frac{\overline{X} - \mu}{\frac{\sigma}{\sqrt{n}}} \sim \mathrm{N}(0,\ 1)$$

For a random sample of n_x observations from $\mathrm{N}(\mu_x,\ \sigma_x^2)$ and, independently, a random sample of n_y observations from $\mathrm{N}(\mu_y,\ \sigma_y^2)$

$$\frac{(\overline{X} - \overline{Y}) - (\mu_x - \mu_y)}{\sqrt{\frac{\sigma_x^2}{n_x} + \frac{\sigma_y^2}{n_y}}} \sim \mathrm{N}(0,\ 1)$$

Correlation and regression

Spearman's rank correlation coefficient is $r_s = 1 - \dfrac{6\sum d^2}{n(n^2 - 1)}$

Non-parametric tests

Goodness-of-fit test and contingency tables: $\displaystyle\sum \frac{(O_i - E_i)^2}{E_i} \sim \chi_\nu^2$

The normal distribution function

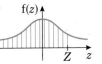

$$\Phi(z) = P(Z < z)$$

z	P(Z < z)	z	P(Z < z)	z	P(Z < z)	z	P(Z < z)	z	P(Z < z)
0.00	0.5000	0.50	0.6915	1.00	0.8413	1.50	0.9332	2.00	0.9772
0.01	0.5040	0.51	0.6950	1.01	0.8438	1.51	0.9345	2.02	0.9783
0.02	0.5080	0.52	0.6985	1.02	0.8461	1.52	0.9357	2.04	0.9793
0.03	0.5120	0.53	0.7019	1.03	0.8485	1.53	0.9370	2.06	0.9803
0.04	0.5160	0.54	0.7054	1.04	0.8508	1.54	0.9382	2.08	0.9812
0.05	0.5199	0.55	0.7088	1.05	0.8531	1.55	0.9394	2.10	0.9821
0.06	0.5239	0.56	0.7123	1.06	0.8554	1.56	0.9406	2.12	0.9830
0.07	0.5279	0.57	0.7157	1.07	0.8577	1.57	0.9418	2.14	0.9838
0.08	0.5319	0.58	0.7190	1.08	0.8599	1.58	0.9429	2.16	0.9846
0.09	0.5359	0.59	0.7224	1.09	0.8621	1.59	0.9441	2.18	0.9854
0.10	0.5398	0.60	0.7257	1.10	0.8643	1.60	0.9452	2.20	0.9861
0.11	0.5438	0.61	0.7291	1.11	0.8665	1.61	0.9463	2.22	0.9868
0.12	0.5478	0.62	0.7324	1.12	0.8686	1.62	0.9474	2.24	0.9875
0.13	0.5517	0.63	0.7357	1.13	0.8708	1.63	0.9484	2.26	0.9881
0.14	0.5557	0.64	0.7389	1.14	0.8729	1.64	0.9495	2.28	0.9887
0.15	0.5596	0.65	0.7422	1.15	0.8749	1.65	0.9505	2.30	0.9893
0.16	0.5636	0.66	0.7454	1.16	0.8770	1.66	0.9515	2.32	0.9898
0.17	0.5675	0.67	0.7486	1.17	0.8790	1.67	0.9525	2.34	0.9904
0.18	0.5714	0.68	0.7517	1.18	0.8810	1.68	0.9535	2.36	0.9909
0.19	0.5753	0.69	0.7549	1.19	0.8830	1.69	0.9545	2.38	0.9913
0.20	0.5793	0.70	0.7580	1.20	0.8849	1.70	0.9554	2.40	0.9918
0.21	0.5832	0.71	0.7611	1.21	0.8869	1.71	0.9564	2.42	0.9922
0.22	0.5871	0.72	0.7642	1.22	0.8888	1.72	0.9573	2.44	0.9927
0.23	0.5910	0.73	0.7673	1.23	0.8907	1.73	0.9582	2.46	0.9931
0.24	0.5948	0.74	0.7704	1.24	0.8925	1.74	0.9591	2.48	0.9934
0.25	0.5987	0.75	0.7734	1.25	0.8944	1.75	0.9599	2.50	0.9938
0.26	0.6026	0.76	0.7764	1.26	0.8962	1.76	0.9608	2.55	0.9946
0.27	0.6064	0.77	0.7794	1.27	0.8980	1.77	0.9616	2.60	0.9953
0.28	0.6103	0.78	0.7823	1.28	0.8997	1.78	0.9625	2.65	0.9960
0.29	0.6141	0.79	0.7852	1.29	0.9015	1.79	0.9633	2.70	0.9965
0.30	0.6179	0.80	0.7881	1.30	0.9032	1.80	0.9641	2.75	0.9970
0.31	0.6217	0.81	0.7910	1.31	0.9049	1.81	0.9649	2.80	0.9974
0.32	0.6255	0.82	0.7939	1.32	0.9066	1.82	0.9656	2.85	0.9978
0.33	0.6293	0.83	0.7967	1.33	0.9082	1.83	0.9664	2.90	0.9981
0.34	0.6331	0.84	0.7995	1.34	0.9099	1.84	0.9671	2.95	0.9984
0.35	0.6368	0.85	0.8023	1.35	0.9115	1.85	0.9678	3.00	0.9987
0.36	0.6406	0.86	0.8051	1.36	0.9131	1.86	0.9686	3.05	0.9989
0.37	0.6443	0.87	0.8078	1.37	0.9147	1.87	0.9693	3.10	0.9990
0.38	0.6480	0.88	0.8106	1.38	0.9162	1.88	0.9699	3.15	0.9992
0.39	0.6517	0.89	0.8133	1.39	0.9177	1.89	0.9706	3.20	0.9993
0.40	0.6554	0.90	0.8159	1.40	0.9192	1.90	0.9713	3.25	0.9994
0.41	0.6591	0.91	0.8186	1.41	0.9207	1.91	0.9719	3.30	0.9995
0.42	0.6628	0.92	0.8212	1.42	0.9222	1.92	0.9726	3.35	0.9996
0.43	0.6664	0.93	0.8238	1.43	0.9236	1.93	0.9732	3.40	0.9997
0.44	0.6700	0.94	0.8264	1.44	0.9251	1.94	0.9738	3.50	0.9998
0.45	0.6736	0.95	0.8289	1.45	0.9265	1.95	0.9744	3.60	0.9998
0.46	0.6772	0.96	0.8315	1.46	0.9279	1.96	0.9750	3.70	0.9999
0.47	0.6808	0.97	0.8340	1.47	0.9292	1.97	0.9756	3.80	0.9999
0.48	0.6844	0.98	0.8365	1.48	0.9306	1.98	0.9761	3.90	1.0000
0.49	0.6879	0.99	0.8389	1.49	0.9319	1.99	0.9767	4.00	1.0000
0.50	0.6915	1.00	0.8413	1.50	0.9332	2.00	0.9772		

Percentage points of the normal distribution

The values z in the table are those which a random variable $Z \sim N(0,1)$ exceeds with probability p; that is, $P(Z > z) = p$.

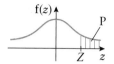

p	z	p	z
0.5000	0.0000	0.0500	1.6449
0.4000	0.2533	0.0250	1.9600
0.3000	0.5244	0.0100	2.3263
0.2000	0.8416	0.0050	2.5758
0.1500	1.0364	0.0010	3.0902
0.1000	1.2816	0.0005	3.2905

Binomial cumulative distribution function

The tabulated value is $P(X \leq x)$, where X has a binomial distribution with index n and parameter p.

	$p =$	0.05	0.10	0.15	0.20	0.25	0.30	0.35	0.40	0.45	0.50
$n = 5, x = 0$		0.7738	0.5905	0.4437	0.3277	0.2373	0.1681	0.1160	0.0778	0.0503	0.0312
	1	0.9774	0.9185	0.8352	0.7373	0.6328	0.5282	0.4284	0.3370	0.2562	0.1875
	2	0.9988	0.9914	0.9734	0.9421	0.8965	0.8369	0.7648	0.6826	0.5931	0.5000
	3	1.0000	0.9995	0.9978	0.9933	0.9844	0.9692	0.9460	0.9130	0.8688	0.8125
	4	1.0000	1.0000	0.9999	0.9997	0.9990	0.9976	0.9947	0.9898	0.9815	0.9688
$n = 6, x = 0$		0.7351	0.5314	0.3771	0.2621	0.1780	0.1176	0.0754	0.0467	0.0277	0.0156
	1	0.9672	0.8857	0.7765	0.6554	0.5339	0.4202	0.3191	0.2333	0.1636	0.1094
	2	0.9978	0.9842	0.9527	0.9011	0.8306	0.7443	0.6471	0.5443	0.4415	0.3438
	3	0.9999	0.9987	0.9941	0.9830	0.9624	0.9295	0.8826	0.8208	0.7447	0.6563
	4	1.0000	0.9999	0.9996	0.9984	0.9954	0.9891	0.9777	0.9590	0.9308	0.8906
	5	1.0000	1.0000	1.0000	0.9999	0.9998	0.9993	0.9982	0.9959	0.9917	0.9844
$n = 7, x = 0$		0.6983	0.4783	0.3206	0.2097	0.1335	0.0824	0.0490	0.0280	0.0152	0.0078
	1	0.9556	0.8503	0.7166	0.5767	0.4449	0.3294	0.2338	0.1586	0.1024	0.0625
	2	0.9962	0.9743	0.9262	0.8520	0.7564	0.6471	0.5323	0.4199	0.3164	0.2266
	3	0.9998	0.9973	0.9879	0.9667	0.9294	0.8740	0.8002	0.7102	0.6083	0.5000
	4	1.0000	0.9998	0.9988	0.9953	0.9871	0.9712	0.9444	0.9037	0.8471	0.7734
	5	1.0000	1.0000	0.9999	0.9996	0.9987	0.9962	0.9910	0.9812	0.9643	0.9375
	6	1.0000	1.0000	1.0000	1.0000	0.9999	0.9998	0.9994	0.9984	0.9963	0.9922
$n = 8, x = 0$		0.6634	0.4305	0.2725	0.1678	0.1001	0.0576	0.0319	0.0168	0.0084	0.0039
	1	0.9428	0.8131	0.6572	0.5033	0.3671	0.2553	0.1691	0.1064	0.0632	0.0352
	2	0.9942	0.9619	0.8948	0.7969	0.6785	0.5518	0.4278	0.3154	0.2201	0.1445
	3	0.9996	0.9950	0.9786	0.9437	0.8862	0.8059	0.7064	0.5941	0.4770	0.3633
	4	1.0000	0.9996	0.9971	0.9896	0.9727	0.9420	0.8939	0.8263	0.7396	0.6367
	5	1.0000	1.0000	0.9998	0.9988	0.9958	0.9887	0.9747	0.9502	0.9115	0.8555
	6	1.0000	1.0000	1.0000	0.9999	0.9996	0.9987	0.9964	0.9915	0.9819	0.9648
	7	1.0000	1.0000	1.0000	1.0000	1.0000	0.9999	0.9998	0.9993	0.9983	0.9961
$n = 9, x = 0$		0.6302	0.3874	0.2316	0.1342	0.0751	0.0404	0.0207	0.0101	0.0046	0.0020
	1	0.9288	0.7748	0.5995	0.4362	0.3003	0.1960	0.1211	0.0705	0.0385	0.0195
	2	0.9916	0.9470	0.8591	0.7382	0.6007	0.4628	0.3373	0.2318	0.1495	0.0898
	3	0.9994	0.9917	0.9661	0.9144	0.8343	0.7297	0.6089	0.4826	0.3614	0.2539
	4	1.0000	0.9991	0.9944	0.9804	0.9511	0.9012	0.8283	0.7334	0.6214	0.5000
	5	1.0000	0.9999	0.9994	0.9969	0.9900	0.9747	0.9464	0.9006	0.8342	0.7461
	6	1.0000	1.0000	1.0000	0.9997	0.9987	0.9957	0.9888	0.9750	0.9502	0.9102
	7	1.0000	1.0000	1.0000	1.0000	0.9999	0.9996	0.9986	0.9962	0.9909	0.9805
	8	1.0000	1.0000	1.0000	1.0000	1.0000	1.0000	0.9999	0.9997	0.9992	0.9980
$n = 10, x = 0$		0.5987	0.3487	0.1969	0.1074	0.0563	0.0282	0.0135	0.0060	0.0025	0.0010
	1	0.9139	0.7361	0.5443	0.3758	0.2440	0.1493	0.0860	0.0464	0.0233	0.0107
	2	0.9885	0.9298	0.8202	0.6778	0.5256	0.3828	0.2616	0.1673	0.0996	0.0547
	3	0.9990	0.9872	0.9500	0.8791	0.7759	0.6496	0.5138	0.3823	0.2660	0.1719
	4	0.9999	0.9984	0.9901	0.9672	0.9219	0.8497	0.7515	0.6331	0.5044	0.3770
	5	1.0000	0.9999	0.9986	0.9936	0.9803	0.9527	0.9051	0.8338	0.7384	0.6230
	6	1.0000	1.0000	0.9999	0.9991	0.9965	0.9894	0.9740	0.9452	0.8980	0.8281
	7	1.0000	1.0000	1.0000	0.9999	0.9996	0.9984	0.9952	0.9877	0.9726	0.9453
	8	1.0000	1.0000	1.0000	1.0000	1.0000	0.9999	0.9995	0.9983	0.9955	0.9893
	9	1.0000	1.0000	1.0000	1.0000	1.0000	1.0000	1.0000	0.9999	0.9997	0.9990

$p =$	0.05	0.10	0.15	0.20	0.25	0.30	0.35	0.40	0.45	0.50
$n = 12, x = 0$	0.5404	0.2824	0.1422	0.0687	0.0317	0.0138	0.0057	0.0022	0.0008	0.0002
1	0.8816	0.6590	0.4435	0.2749	0.1584	0.0850	0.0424	0.0196	0.0083	0.0032
2	0.9804	0.8891	0.7358	0.5583	0.3907	0.2528	0.1513	0.0834	0.0421	0.0193
3	0.9978	0.9744	0.9078	0.7946	0.6488	0.4925	0.3467	0.2253	0.1345	0.0730
4	0.9998	0.9957	0.9761	0.9274	0.8424	0.7237	0.5833	0.4382	0.3044	0.1938
5	1.0000	0.9995	0.9954	0.9806	0.9456	0.8822	0.7873	0.6652	0.5269	0.3872
6	1.0000	0.9999	0.9993	0.9961	0.9857	0.9614	0.9154	0.8418	0.7393	0.6128
7	1.0000	1.0000	0.9999	0.9994	0.9972	0.9905	0.9745	0.9427	0.8883	0.8062
8	1.0000	1.0000	1.0000	0.9999	0.9996	0.9983	0.9944	0.9847	0.9644	0.9270
9	1.0000	1.0000	1.0000	1.0000	1.0000	0.9998	0.9992	0.9972	0.9921	0.9807
10	1.0000	1.0000	1.0000	1.0000	1.0000	1.0000	0.9999	0.9997	0.9989	0.9968
11	1.0000	1.0000	1.0000	1.0000	1.0000	1.0000	1.0000	1.0000	0.9999	0.9998
$n = 15, x = 0$	0.4633	0.2059	0.0874	0.0352	0.0134	0.0047	0.0016	0.0005	0.0001	0.0000
1	0.8290	0.5490	0.3186	0.1671	0.0802	0.0353	0.0142	0.0052	0.0017	0.0005
2	0.9638	0.8159	0.6042	0.3980	0.2361	0.1268	0.0617	0.0271	0.0107	0.0037
3	0.9945	0.9444	0.8227	0.6482	0.4613	0.2969	0.1727	0.0905	0.0424	0.0176
4	0.9994	0.9873	0.9383	0.8358	0.6865	0.5155	0.3519	0.2173	0.1204	0.0592
5	0.9999	0.9978	0.9832	0.9389	0.8516	0.7216	0.5643	0.4032	0.2608	0.1509
6	1.0000	0.9997	0.9964	0.9819	0.9434	0.8689	0.7548	0.6098	0.4522	0.3036
7	1.0000	1.0000	0.9994	0.9958	0.9827	0.9500	0.8868	0.7869	0.6535	0.5000
8	1.0000	1.0000	0.9999	0.9992	0.9958	0.9848	0.9578	0.9050	0.8182	0.6964
9	1.0000	1.0000	1.0000	0.9999	0.9992	0.9963	0.9876	0.9662	0.9231	0.8491
10	1.0000	1.0000	1.0000	1.0000	0.9999	0.9993	0.9972	0.9907	0.9745	0.9408
11	1.0000	1.0000	1.0000	1.0000	1.0000	0.9999	0.9995	0.9981	0.9937	0.9824
12	1.0000	1.0000	1.0000	1.0000	1.0000	1.0000	0.9999	0.9997	0.9989	0.9963
13	1.0000	1.0000	1.0000	1.0000	1.0000	1.0000	1.0000	1.0000	0.9999	0.9995
14	1.0000	1.0000	1.0000	1.0000	1.0000	1.0000	1.0000	1.0000	1.0000	1.0000
$n = 20, x = 0$	0.3585	0.1216	0.0388	0.0115	0.0032	0.0008	0.0002	0.0000	0.0000	0.0000
1	0.7358	0.3917	0.1756	0.0692	0.0243	0.0076	0.0021	0.0005	0.0001	0.0000
2	0.9245	0.6769	0.4049	0.2061	0.0913	0.0355	0.0121	0.0036	0.0009	0.0002
3	0.9841	0.8670	0.6477	0.4114	0.2252	0.1071	0.0444	0.0160	0.0049	0.0013
4	0.9974	0.9568	0.8298	0.6296	0.4148	0.2375	0.1182	0.0510	0.0189	0.0059
5	0.9997	0.9887	0.9327	0.8042	0.6172	0.4164	0.2454	0.1256	0.0553	0.0207
6	1.0000	0.9976	0.9781	0.9133	0.7858	0.6080	0.4166	0.2500	0.1299	0.0577
7	1.0000	0.9996	0.9941	0.9679	0.8982	0.7723	0.6010	0.4159	0.2520	0.1316
8	1.0000	0.9999	0.9987	0.9900	0.9591	0.8867	0.7624	0.5956	0.4143	0.2517
9	1.0000	1.0000	0.9998	0.9974	0.9861	0.9520	0.8782	0.7553	0.5914	0.4119
10	1.0000	1.0000	1.0000	0.9994	0.9961	0.9829	0.9468	0.8725	0.7507	0.5881
11	1.0000	1.0000	1.0000	0.9999	0.9991	0.9949	0.9804	0.9435	0.8692	0.7483
12	1.0000	1.0000	1.0000	1.0000	0.9998	0.9987	0.9940	0.9790	0.9420	0.8684
13	1.0000	1.0000	1.0000	1.0000	1.0000	0.9997	0.9985	0.9935	0.9786	0.9423
14	1.0000	1.0000	1.0000	1.0000	1.0000	1.0000	0.9997	0.9984	0.9936	0.9793
15	1.0000	1.0000	1.0000	1.0000	1.0000	1.0000	1.0000	0.9997	0.9985	0.9941
16	1.0000	1.0000	1.0000	1.0000	1.0000	1.0000	1.0000	1.0000	0.9997	0.9987
17	1.0000	1.0000	1.0000	1.0000	1.0000	1.0000	1.0000	1.0000	1.0000	0.9998
18	1.0000	1.0000	1.0000	1.0000	1.0000	1.0000	1.0000	1.0000	1.0000	1.0000

p =	0.05	0.10	0.15	0.20	0.25	0.30	0.35	0.40	0.45	0.50
n = 25, x = 0	0.2774	0.0718	0.0172	0.0038	0.0008	0.0001	0.0000	0.0000	0.0000	0.0000
1	0.6424	0.2712	0.0931	0.0274	0.0070	0.0016	0.0003	0.0001	0.0000	0.0000
2	0.8729	0.5371	0.2537	0.0982	0.0321	0.0090	0.0021	0.0004	0.0001	0.0000
3	0.9659	0.7636	0.4711	0.2340	0.0962	0.0332	0.0097	0.0024	0.0005	0.0001
4	0.9928	0.9020	0.6821	0.4207	0.2137	0.0905	0.0320	0.0095	0.0023	0.0005
5	0.9988	0.9666	0.8385	0.6167	0.3783	0.1935	0.0826	0.0294	0.0086	0.0020
6	0.9998	0.9905	0.9305	0.7800	0.5611	0.3407	0.1734	0.0736	0.0258	0.0073
7	1.0000	0.9977	0.9745	0.8909	0.7265	0.5118	0.3061	0.1536	0.0639	0.0216
8	1.0000	0.9995	0.9920	0.9532	0.8506	0.6769	0.4668	0.2735	0.1340	0.0539
9	1.0000	0.9999	0.9979	0.9827	0.9287	0.8106	0.6303	0.4246	0.2424	0.1148
10	1.0000	1.0000	0.9995	0.9944	0.9703	0.9022	0.7712	0.5858	0.3843	0.2122
11	1.0000	1.0000	0.9999	0.9985	0.9893	0.9558	0.8746	0.7323	0.5426	0.3450
12	1.0000	1.0000	1.0000	0.9996	0.9966	0.9825	0.9396	0.8462	0.6937	0.5000
13	1.0000	1.0000	1.0000	0.9999	0.9991	0.9940	0.9745	0.9222	0.8173	0.6550
14	1.0000	1.0000	1.0000	1.0000	0.9998	0.9982	0.9907	0.9656	0.9040	0.7878
15	1.0000	1.0000	1.0000	1.0000	1.0000	0.9995	0.9971	0.9868	0.9560	0.8852
16	1.0000	1.0000	1.0000	1.0000	1.0000	0.9999	0.9992	0.9957	0.9826	0.9461
17	1.0000	1.0000	1.0000	1.0000	1.0000	1.0000	0.9998	0.9988	0.9942	0.9784
18	1.0000	1.0000	1.0000	1.0000	1.0000	1.0000	1.0000	0.9997	0.9984	0.9927
19	1.0000	1.0000	1.0000	1.0000	1.0000	1.0000	1.0000	0.9999	0.9996	0.9980
20	1.0000	1.0000	1.0000	1.0000	1.0000	1.0000	1.0000	1.0000	0.9999	0.9995
21	1.0000	1.0000	1.0000	1.0000	1.0000	1.0000	1.0000	1.0000	1.0000	0.9999
22	1.0000	1.0000	1.0000	1.0000	1.0000	1.0000	1.0000	1.0000	1.0000	1.0000
n = 30, x = 0	0.2146	0.0424	0.0076	0.0012	0.0002	0.0000	0.0000	0.0000	0.0000	0.0000
1	0.5535	0.1837	0.0480	0.0105	0.0020	0.0003	0.0000	0.0000	0.0000	0.0000
2	0.8122	0.4114	0.1514	0.0442	0.0106	0.0021	0.0003	0.0000	0.0000	0.0000
3	0.9392	0.6474	0.3217	0.1227	0.0374	0.0093	0.0019	0.0003	0.0000	0.0000
4	0.9844	0.8245	0.5245	0.2552	0.0979	0.0302	0.0075	0.0015	0.0002	0.0000
5	0.9967	0.9268	0.7106	0.4275	0.2026	0.0766	0.0233	0.0057	0.0011	0.0002
6	0.9994	0.9742	0.8474	0.6070	0.3481	0.1595	0.0586	0.0172	0.0040	0.0007
7	0.9999	0.9922	0.9302	0.7608	0.5143	0.2814	0.1238	0.0435	0.0121	0.0026
8	1.0000	0.9980	0.9722	0.8713	0.6736	0.4315	0.2247	0.0940	0.0312	0.0081
9	1.0000	0.9995	0.9903	0.9389	0.8034	0.5888	0.3575	0.1763	0.0694	0.0214
10	1.0000	0.9999	0.9971	0.9744	0.8943	0.7304	0.5078	0.2915	0.1350	0.0494
11	1.0000	1.0000	0.9992	0.9905	0.9493	0.8407	0.6548	0.4311	0.2327	0.1002
12	1.0000	1.0000	0.9998	0.9969	0.9784	0.9155	0.7802	0.5785	0.3592	0.1808
13	1.0000	1.0000	1.0000	0.9991	0.9918	0.9599	0.8737	0.7145	0.5025	0.2923
14	1.0000	1.0000	1.0000	0.9998	0.9973	0.9831	0.9348	0.8246	0.6448	0.4278
15	1.0000	1.0000	1.0000	0.9999	0.9992	0.9936	0.9699	0.9029	0.7691	0.5722
16	1.0000	1.0000	1.0000	1.0000	0.9998	0.9979	0.9876	0.9519	0.8644	0.7077
17	1.0000	1.0000	1.0000	1.0000	0.9999	0.9994	0.9955	0.9788	0.9286	0.8192
18	1.0000	1.0000	1.0000	1.0000	1.0000	0.9998	0.9986	0.9917	0.9666	0.8998
19	1.0000	1.0000	1.0000	1.0000	1.0000	1.0000	0.9996	0.9971	0.9862	0.9506
20	1.0000	1.0000	1.0000	1.0000	1.0000	1.0000	0.9999	0.9991	0.9950	0.9786
21	1.0000	1.0000	1.0000	1.0000	1.0000	1.0000	1.0000	0.9998	0.9984	0.9919
22	1.0000	1.0000	1.0000	1.0000	1.0000	1.0000	1.0000	1.0000	0.9996	0.9974
23	1.0000	1.0000	1.0000	1.0000	1.0000	1.0000	1.0000	1.0000	0.9999	0.9993
24	1.0000	1.0000	1.0000	1.0000	1.0000	1.0000	1.0000	1.0000	1.0000	0.9998
25	1.0000	1.0000	1.0000	1.0000	1.0000	1.0000	1.0000	1.0000	1.0000	1.0000

$p =$	0.05	0.10	0.15	0.20	0.25	0.30	0.35	0.40	0.45	0.50
$n = 40, x = 0$	0.1285	0.0148	0.0015	0.0001	0.0000	0.0000	0.0000	0.0000	0.0000	0.0000
1	0.3991	0.0805	0.0121	0.0015	0.0001	0.0000	0.0000	0.0000	0.0000	0.0000
2	0.6767	0.2228	0.0486	0.0079	0.0010	0.0001	0.0000	0.0000	0.0000	0.0000
3	0.8619	0.4231	0.1302	0.0285	0.0047	0.0006	0.0001	0.0000	0.0000	0.0000
4	0.9520	0.6290	0.2633	0.0759	0.0160	0.0026	0.0003	0.0000	0.0000	0.0000
5	0.9861	0.7937	0.4325	0.1613	0.0433	0.0086	0.0013	0.0001	0.0000	0.0000
6	0.9966	0.9005	0.6067	0.2859	0.0962	0.0238	0.0044	0.0006	0.0001	0.0000
7	0.9993	0.9581	0.7559	0.4371	0.1820	0.0553	0.0124	0.0021	0.0002	0.0000
8	0.9999	0.9845	0.8646	0.5931	0.2998	0.1110	0.0303	0.0061	0.0009	0.0001
9	1.0000	0.9949	0.9328	0.7318	0.4395	0.1959	0.0644	0.0156	0.0027	0.0003
10	1.0000	0.9985	0.9701	0.8392	0.5839	0.3087	0.1215	0.0352	0.0074	0.0011
11	1.0000	0.9996	0.9880	0.9125	0.7151	0.4406	0.2053	0.0709	0.0179	0.0032
12	1.0000	0.9999	0.9957	0.9568	0.8209	0.5772	0.3143	0.1285	0.0386	0.0083
13	1.0000	1.0000	0.9986	0.9806	0.8968	0.7032	0.4408	0.2112	0.0751	0.0192
14	1.0000	1.0000	0.9996	0.9921	0.9456	0.8074	0.5721	0.3174	0.1326	0.0403
15	1.0000	1.0000	0.9999	0.9971	0.9738	0.8849	0.6946	0.4402	0.2142	0.0769
16	1.0000	1.0000	1.0000	0.9990	0.9884	0.9367	0.7978	0.5681	0.3185	0.1341
17	1.0000	1.0000	1.0000	0.9997	0.9953	0.9680	0.8761	0.6885	0.4391	0.2148
18	1.0000	1.0000	1.0000	0.9999	0.9983	0.9852	0.9301	0.7911	0.5651	0.3179
19	1.0000	1.0000	1.0000	1.0000	0.9994	0.9937	0.9637	0.8702	0.6844	0.4373
20	1.0000	1.0000	1.0000	1.0000	0.9998	0.9976	0.9827	0.9256	0.7870	0.5627
21	1.0000	1.0000	1.0000	1.0000	1.0000	0.9991	0.9925	0.9608	0.8669	0.6821
22	1.0000	1.0000	1.0000	1.0000	1.0000	0.9997	0.9970	0.9811	0.9233	0.7852
23	1.0000	1.0000	1.0000	1.0000	1.0000	0.9999	0.9989	0.9917	0.9595	0.8659
24	1.0000	1.0000	1.0000	1.0000	1.0000	1.0000	0.9996	0.9966	0.9804	0.9231
25	1.0000	1.0000	1.0000	1.0000	1.0000	1.0000	0.9999	0.9988	0.9914	0.9597
26	1.0000	1.0000	1.0000	1.0000	1.0000	1.0000	1.0000	0.9996	0.9966	0.9808
27	1.0000	1.0000	1.0000	1.0000	1.0000	1.0000	1.0000	0.9999	0.9988	0.9917
28	1.0000	1.0000	1.0000	1.0000	1.0000	1.0000	1.0000	1.0000	0.9996	0.9968
29	1.0000	1.0000	1.0000	1.0000	1.0000	1.0000	1.0000	1.0000	0.9999	0.9989
30	1.0000	1.0000	1.0000	1.0000	1.0000	1.0000	1.0000	1.0000	1.0000	0.9997
31	1.0000	1.0000	1.0000	1.0000	1.0000	1.0000	1.0000	1.0000	1.0000	0.9999
32	1.0000	1.0000	1.0000	1.0000	1.0000	1.0000	1.0000	1.0000	1.0000	1.0000

$p =$	0.05	0.10	0.15	0.20	0.25	0.30	0.35	0.40	0.45	0.50
$n = 50, x = 0$	0.0769	0.0052	0.0003	0.0000	0.0000	0.0000	0.0000	0.0000	0.0000	0.0000
1	0.2794	0.0338	0.0029	0.0002	0.0000	0.0000	0.0000	0.0000	0.0000	0.0000
2	0.5405	0.1117	0.0142	0.0013	0.0001	0.0000	0.0000	0.0000	0.0000	0.0000
3	0.7604	0.2503	0.0460	0.0057	0.0005	0.0000	0.0000	0.0000	0.0000	0.0000
4	0.8964	0.4312	0.1121	0.0185	0.0021	0.0002	0.0000	0.0000	0.0000	0.0000
5	0.9622	0.6161	0.2194	0.0480	0.0070	0.0007	0.0001	0.0000	0.0000	0.0000
6	0.9882	0.7702	0.3613	0.1034	0.0194	0.0025	0.0002	0.0000	0.0000	0.0000
7	0.9968	0.8779	0.5188	0.1904	0.0453	0.0073	0.0008	0.0001	0.0000	0.0000
8	0.9992	0.9421	0.6681	0.3073	0.0916	0.0183	0.0025	0.0002	0.0000	0.0000
9	0.9998	0.9755	0.7911	0.4437	0.1637	0.0402	0.0067	0.0008	0.0001	0.0000
10	1.0000	0.9906	0.8801	0.5836	0.2622	0.0789	0.0160	0.0022	0.0002	0.0000
11	1.0000	0.9968	0.9372	0.7107	0.3816	0.1390	0.0342	0.0057	0.0006	0.0000
12	1.0000	0.9990	0.9699	0.8139	0.5110	0.2229	0.0661	0.0133	0.0018	0.0002
13	1.0000	0.9997	0.9868	0.8894	0.6370	0.3279	0.1163	0.0280	0.0045	0.0005
14	1.0000	0.9999	0.9947	0.9393	0.7481	0.4468	0.1878	0.0540	0.0104	0.0013
15	1.0000	1.0000	0.9981	0.9692	0.8369	0.5692	0.2801	0.0955	0.0220	0.0033
16	1.0000	1.0000	0.9993	0.9856	0.9017	0.6839	0.3889	0.1561	0.0427	0.0077
17	1.0000	1.0000	0.9998	0.9937	0.9449	0.7822	0.5060	0.2369	0.0765	0.0164
18	1.0000	1.0000	0.9999	0.9975	0.9713	0.8594	0.6216	0.3356	0.1273	0.0325
19	1.0000	1.0000	1.0000	0.9991	0.9861	0.9152	0.7264	0.4465	0.1974	0.0595
20	1.0000	1.0000	1.0000	0.9997	0.9937	0.9522	0.8139	0.5610	0.2862	0.1013
21	1.0000	1.0000	1.0000	0.9999	0.9974	0.9749	0.8813	0.6701	0.3900	0.1611
22	1.0000	1.0000	1.0000	1.0000	0.9990	0.9877	0.9290	0.7660	0.5019	0.2399
23	1.0000	1.0000	1.0000	1.0000	0.9996	0.9944	0.9604	0.8438	0.6134	0.3359
24	1.0000	1.0000	1.0000	1.0000	0.9999	0.9976	0.9793	0.9022	0.7160	0.4439
25	1.0000	1.0000	1.0000	1.0000	1.0000	0.9991	0.9900	0.9427	0.8034	0.5561
26	1.0000	1.0000	1.0000	1.0000	1.0000	0.9997	0.9955	0.9686	0.8721	0.6641
27	1.0000	1.0000	1.0000	1.0000	1.0000	0.9999	0.9981	0.9840	0.9220	0.7601
28	1.0000	1.0000	1.0000	1.0000	1.0000	1.0000	0.9993	0.9924	0.9556	0.8389
29	1.0000	1.0000	1.0000	1.0000	1.0000	1.0000	0.9997	0.9966	0.9765	0.8987
30	1.0000	1.0000	1.0000	1.0000	1.0000	1.0000	0.9999	0.9986	0.9884	0.9405
31	1.0000	1.0000	1.0000	1.0000	1.0000	1.0000	1.0000	0.9995	0.9947	0.9675
32	1.0000	1.0000	1.0000	1.0000	1.0000	1.0000	1.0000	0.9998	0.9978	0.9836
33	1.0000	1.0000	1.0000	1.0000	1.0000	1.0000	1.0000	0.9999	0.9991	0.9923
34	1.0000	1.0000	1.0000	1.0000	1.0000	1.0000	1.0000	1.0000	0.9997	0.9967
35	1.0000	1.0000	1.0000	1.0000	1.0000	1.0000	1.0000	1.0000	0.9999	0.9987
36	1.0000	1.0000	1.0000	1.0000	1.0000	1.0000	1.0000	1.0000	1.0000	0.9995
37	1.0000	1.0000	1.0000	1.0000	1.0000	1.0000	1.0000	1.0000	1.0000	0.9998
38	1.0000	1.0000	1.0000	1.0000	1.0000	1.0000	1.0000	1.0000	1.0000	1.0000

POISSON CUMULATIVE DISTRIBUTION FUNCTION

The tabulated value is $P(X \leq x)$, where X has a Poisson distribution with parameter λ.

$\lambda =$	0.5	1.0	1.5	2.0	2.5	3.0	3.5	4.0	4.5	5.0
$x = 0$	0.6065	0.3679	0.2231	0.1353	0.0821	0.0498	0.0302	0.0183	0.0111	0.0067
1	0.9098	0.7358	0.5578	0.4060	0.2873	0.1991	0.1359	0.0916	0.0611	0.0404
2	0.9856	0.9197	0.8088	0.6767	0.5438	0.4232	0.3208	0.2381	0.1736	0.1247
3	0.9982	0.9810	0.9344	0.8571	0.7576	0.6472	0.5366	0.4335	0.3423	0.2650
4	0.9998	0.9963	0.9814	0.9473	0.8912	0.8153	0.7254	0.6288	0.5321	0.4405
5	1.0000	0.9994	0.9955	0.9834	0.9580	0.9161	0.8576	0.7851	0.7029	0.6160
6	1.0000	0.9999	0.9991	0.9955	0.9858	0.9665	0.9347	0.8893	0.8311	0.7622
7	1.0000	1.0000	0.9998	0.9989	0.9958	0.9881	0.9733	0.9489	0.9134	0.8666
8	1.0000	1.0000	1.0000	0.9998	0.9989	0.9962	0.9901	0.9786	0.9597	0.9319
9	1.0000	1.0000	1.0000	1.0000	0.9997	0.9989	0.9967	0.9919	0.9829	0.9682
10	1.0000	1.0000	1.0000	1.0000	0.9999	0.9997	0.9990	0.9972	0.9933	0.9863
11	1.0000	1.0000	1.0000	1.0000	1.0000	0.9999	0.9997	0.9991	0.9976	0.9945
12	1.0000	1.0000	1.0000	1.0000	1.0000	1.0000	0.9999	0.9997	0.9992	0.9980
13	1.0000	1.0000	1.0000	1.0000	1.0000	1.0000	1.0000	0.9999	0.9997	0.9993
14	1.0000	1.0000	1.0000	1.0000	1.0000	1.0000	1.0000	1.0000	0.9999	0.9998
15	1.0000	1.0000	1.0000	1.0000	1.0000	1.0000	1.0000	1.0000	1.0000	0.9999
16	1.0000	1.0000	1.0000	1.0000	1.0000	1.0000	1.0000	1.0000	1.0000	1.0000
17	1.0000	1.0000	1.0000	1.0000	1.0000	1.0000	1.0000	1.0000	1.0000	1.0000
18	1.0000	1.0000	1.0000	1.0000	1.0000	1.0000	1.0000	1.0000	1.0000	1.0000
19	1.0000	1.0000	1.0000	1.0000	1.0000	1.0000	1.0000	1.0000	1.0000	1.0000

$\lambda =$	5.5	6.0	6.5	7.0	7.5	8.0	8.5	9.0	9.5	10.0
$x = 0$	0.0041	0.0025	0.0015	0.0009	0.0006	0.0003	0.0002	0.0001	0.0001	0.0000
1	0.0266	0.0174	0.0113	0.0073	0.0047	0.0030	0.0019	0.0012	0.0008	0.0005
2	0.0884	0.0620	0.0430	0.0296	0.0203	0.0138	0.0093	0.0062	0.0042	0.0028
3	0.2017	0.1512	0.1118	0.0818	0.0591	0.0424	0.0301	0.0212	0.0149	0.0103
4	0.3575	0.2851	0.2237	0.1730	0.1321	0.0996	0.0744	0.0550	0.0403	0.0293
5	0.5289	0.4457	0.3690	0.3007	0.2414	0.1912	0.1496	0.1157	0.0885	0.0671
6	0.6860	0.6063	0.5265	0.4497	0.3782	0.3134	0.2562	0.2068	0.1649	0.1301
7	0.8095	0.7440	0.6728	0.5987	0.5246	0.4530	0.3856	0.3239	0.2687	0.2202
8	0.8944	0.8472	0.7916	0.7291	0.6620	0.5925	0.5231	0.4557	0.3918	0.3328
9	0.9462	0.9161	0.8774	0.8305	0.7764	0.7166	0.6530	0.5874	0.5218	0.4579
10	0.9747	0.9574	0.9332	0.9015	0.8622	0.8159	0.7634	0.7060	0.6453	0.5830
11	0.9890	0.9799	0.9661	0.9467	0.9208	0.8881	0.8487	0.8030	0.7520	0.6968
12	0.9955	0.9912	0.9840	0.9730	0.9573	0.9362	0.9091	0.8758	0.8364	0.7916
13	0.9983	0.9964	0.9929	0.9872	0.9784	0.9658	0.9486	0.9261	0.8981	0.8645
14	0.9994	0.9986	0.9970	0.9943	0.9897	0.9827	0.9726	0.9585	0.9400	0.9165
15	0.9998	0.9995	0.9988	0.9976	0.9954	0.9918	0.9862	0.9780	0.9665	0.9513
16	0.9999	0.9998	0.9996	0.9990	0.9980	0.9963	0.9934	0.9889	0.9823	0.9730
17	1.0000	0.9999	0.9998	0.9996	0.9992	0.9984	0.9970	0.9947	0.9911	0.9857
18	1.0000	1.0000	0.9999	0.9999	0.9997	0.9993	0.9987	0.9976	0.9957	0.9928
19	1.0000	1.0000	1.0000	1.0000	0.9999	0.9997	0.9995	0.9989	0.9980	0.9965
20	1.0000	1.0000	1.0000	1.0000	1.0000	0.9999	0.9998	0.9996	0.9991	0.9984
21	1.0000	1.0000	1.0000	1.0000	1.0000	1.0000	0.9999	0.9998	0.9996	0.9993
22	1.0000	1.0000	1.0000	1.0000	1.0000	1.0000	1.0000	0.9999	0.9999	0.9997

PERCENTAGE POINTS OF THE χ^2 DISTRIBUTION

The values in the table are those which a random variable with the χ^2 distribution on ν degrees of freedom exceeds with the probability shown.

ν	0.995	0.990	0.975	0.950	0.900	0.100	0.050	0.025	0.010	0.005
1	0.000	0.000	0.001	0.004	0.016	2.705	3.841	5.024	6.635	7.879
2	0.010	0.020	0.051	0.103	0.211	4.605	5.991	7.378	9.210	10.597
3	0.072	0.115	0.216	0.352	0.584	6.251	7.815	9.348	11.345	12.838
4	0.207	0.297	0.484	0.711	1.064	7.779	9.488	11.143	13.277	14.860
5	0.412	0.554	0.831	1.145	1.610	9.236	11.070	12.832	15.086	16.750
6	0.676	0.872	1.237	1.635	2.204	10.645	12.592	14.449	16.812	18.548
7	0.989	1.239	1.690	2.167	2.833	12.017	14.067	16.013	18.475	20.278
8	1.344	1.646	2.180	2.733	3.490	13.362	15.507	17.535	20.090	21.955
9	1.735	2.088	2.700	3.325	4.168	14.684	16.919	19.023	21.666	23.589
10	2.156	2.558	3.247	3.940	4.865	15.987	18.307	20.483	23.209	25.188
11	2.603	3.053	3.816	4.575	5.580	17.275	19.675	21.920	24.725	26.757
12	3.074	3.571	4.404	5.226	6.304	18.549	21.026	23.337	26.217	28.300
13	3.565	4.107	5.009	5.892	7.042	19.812	22.362	24.736	27.688	29.819
14	4.075	4.660	5.629	6.571	7.790	21.064	23.685	26.119	29.141	31.319
15	4.601	5.229	6.262	7.261	8.547	22.307	24.996	27.488	30.578	32.801
16	5.142	5.812	6.908	7.962	9.312	23.542	26.296	28.845	32.000	34.267
17	5.697	6.408	7.564	8.672	10.085	24.769	27.587	30.191	33.409	35.718
18	6.265	7.015	8.231	9.390	10.865	25.989	28.869	31.526	34.805	37.156
19	6.844	7.633	8.907	10.117	11.651	27.204	30.144	32.852	36.191	38.582
20	7.434	8.260	9.591	10.851	12.443	28.412	31.410	34.170	37.566	39.997
21	8.034	8.897	10.283	11.591	13.240	29.615	32.671	35.479	38.932	41.401
22	8.643	9.542	10.982	12.338	14.042	30.813	33.924	36.781	40.289	42.796
23	9.260	10.196	11.689	13.091	14.848	32.007	35.172	38.076	41.638	44.181
24	9.886	10.856	12.401	13.848	15.659	33.196	36.415	39.364	42.980	45.558
25	10.520	11.524	13.120	14.611	16.473	34.382	37.652	40.646	44.314	46.928
26	11.160	12.198	13.844	15.379	17.292	35.563	38.885	41.923	45.642	48.290
27	11.808	12.879	14.573	16.151	18.114	36.741	40.113	43.194	46.963	49.645
28	12.461	13.565	15.308	16.928	18.939	37.916	41.337	44.461	48.278	50.993
29	13.121	14.256	16.047	17.708	19.768	39.088	42.557	45.722	49.588	52.336
30	13.787	14.953	16.791	18.493	20.599	40.256	43.773	46.979	50.892	53.672

CRITICAL VALUES FOR CORRELATION COEFFICIENTS

These tables concern tests of the hypothesis that a population correlation coefficient ρ is 0. The values in the tables are the minimum values which need to be reached by a sample correlation coefficient in order to be significant at the level shown, on a one-tailed test.

Product-Moment Coefficient					Sample	Spearman's Coefficient		
Level					Sample	Level		
0.10	0.05	0.025	0.01	0.005	Level	0.05	0.025	0.01
0.8000	0.9000	0.9500	0.9800	0.9900	4	1.0000	–	–
0.6870	0.8054	0.8783	0.9343	0.9587	5	0.9000	1.0000	1.0000
0.6084	0.7293	0.8114	0.8822	0.9172	6	0.8286	0.8857	0.9429
0.5509	0.6694	0.7545	0.8329	0.8745	7	0.7143	0.7857	0.8929
0.5067	0.6215	0.7067	0.7887	0.8343	8	0.6429	0.7381	0.8333
0.4716	0.5822	0.6664	0.7498	0.7977	9	0.6000	0.7000	0.7833
0.4428	0.5494	0.6319	0.7155	0.7646	10	0.5636	0.6485	0.7455
0.4187	0.5214	0.6021	0.6851	0.7348	11	0.5364	0.6182	0.7091
0.3981	0.4973	0.5760	0.6581	0.7079	12	0.5035	0.5874	0.6783
0.3802	0.4762	0.5529	0.6339	0.6835	13	0.4835	0.5604	0.6484
0.3646	0.4575	0.5324	0.6120	0.6614	14	0.4637	0.5385	0.6264
0.3507	0.4409	0.5140	0.5923	0.6411	15	0.4464	0.5214	0.6036
0.3383	0.4259	0.4973	0.5742	0.6226	16	0.4294	0.5029	0.5824
0.3271	0.4124	0.4821	0.5577	0.6055	17	0.4142	0.4877	0.5662
0.3170	0.4000	0.4683	0.5425	0.5897	18	0.4014	0.4716	0.5501
0.3077	0.3887	0.4555	0.5285	0.5751	19	0.3912	0.4596	0.5351
0.2992	0.3783	0.4438	0.5155	0.5614	20	0.3805	0.4466	0.5218
0.2914	0.3687	0.4329	0.5034	0.5487	21	0.3701	0.4364	0.5091
0.2841	0.3598	0.4227	0.4921	0.5368	22	0.3608	0.4252	0.4975
0.2774	0.3515	0.4133	0.4815	0.5256	23	0.3528	0.4160	0.4862
0.2711	0.3438	0.4044	0.4716	0.5151	24	0.3443	0.4070	0.4757
0.2653	0.3365	0.3961	0.4622	0.5052	25	0.3369	0.3977	0.4662
0.2598	0.3297	0.3882	0.4534	0.4958	26	0.3306	0.3901	0.4571
0.2546	0.3233	0.3809	0.4451	0.4869	27	0.3242	0.3828	0.4487
0.2497	0.3172	0.3739	0.4372	0.4785	28	0.3180	0.3755	0.4401
0.2451	0.3115	0.3673	0.4297	0.4705	29	0.3118	0.3685	0.4325
0.2407	0.3061	0.3610	0.4226	0.4629	30	0.3063	0.3624	0.4251
0.2070	0.2638	0.3120	0.3665	0.4026	40	0.2640	0.3128	0.3681
0.1843	0.2353	0.2787	0.3281	0.3610	50	0.2353	0.2791	0.3293
0.1678	0.2144	0.2542	0.2997	0.3301	60	0.2144	0.2545	0.3005
0.1550	0.1982	0.2352	0.2776	0.3060	70	0.1982	0.2354	0.2782
0.1448	0.1852	0.2199	0.2597	0.2864	80	0.1852	0.2201	0.2602
0.1364	0.1745	0.2072	0.2449	0.2702	90	0.1745	0.2074	0.2453
0.1292	0.1654	0.1966	0.2324	0.2565	100	0.1654	0.1967	0.2327

RANDOM NUMBERS

86	13	84	10	07	30	39	05	97	96	88	07	37	26	04	89	13	48	19	20
60	78	48	12	99	47	09	46	91	33	17	21	03	94	79	00	08	50	40	16
78	48	06	37	82	26	01	06	64	65	94	41	17	26	74	66	61	93	24	97
80	56	90	79	66	94	18	40	97	79	93	20	41	51	25	04	20	71	76	04
99	09	39	25	66	31	70	56	30	15	52	17	87	55	31	11	10	68	98	23
56	32	32	72	91	65	97	36	56	61	12	79	95	17	57	16	53	58	96	36
66	02	49	93	97	44	99	15	56	86	80	57	11	78	40	23	58	40	86	14
31	77	53	94	05	93	56	14	71	23	60	46	05	33	23	72	93	10	81	23
98	79	72	43	14	76	54	77	66	29	84	09	88	56	75	86	41	67	04	42
50	97	92	15	10	01	57	01	87	33	73	17	70	18	40	21	24	20	66	62
90	51	94	50	12	48	88	95	09	34	09	30	22	27	25	56	40	76	01	59
31	99	52	24	13	43	27	88	11	39	41	65	00	84	13	06	31	79	74	97
22	96	23	34	46	12	67	11	48	06	99	24	14	83	78	37	65	73	39	47
06	84	55	41	27	06	74	59	14	29	20	14	45	75	31	16	05	41	22	96
08	64	89	30	25	25	71	35	33	31	04	56	12	67	03	74	07	16	49	32
86	87	62	43	15	11	76	49	79	13	78	80	93	89	09	57	07	14	40	74
94	44	97	13	77	04	35	02	12	76	60	91	93	40	81	06	85	85	72	84
63	25	55	14	66	47	99	90	02	90	83	43	16	01	19	69	11	78	87	16
11	22	83	98	15	21	18	57	53	42	91	91	26	52	89	13	86	00	47	61
01	70	10	83	94	71	13	67	11	12	36	54	53	32	90	43	79	01	95	15

Answers

Exercise 1A

1 a $W \sim N(130, 13)$
  b $W \sim N(30, 13)$
2 $R \sim N(148, 18)$
3 a $T \sim N(180, 225)$ or $N(180, 15^2)$
  b $T \sim N(350, 784)$ or $N(350, 28^2)$
  c $T \sim N(530, 1009)$
  d $T \sim N(-40, 89)$
4 a $A \sim N(35, 9)$ or $N(35, 3^2)$
  b $A \sim N(7, 6)$
  c $A \sim N(41, 41)$
  d $A \sim N(84, 82)$
  e $A \sim N(19, 15)$
5 a awrt 0.91
  b 0.0516 (0.0512)
  c awrt 0.319
  d 0.0618 (0.0614)
  e awrt 0.858 (0.857)
  f awrt 0.855
6 a 10
  b 9
  c awrt 0.136
7 a 64
  b 148
  c 0.0294 (0.0293)
  d 28
8 0.0384 (0.0385)
9 0.0537
10 a i awrt 0.268
   ii awrt 0.436
  b 37.1
11 a awrt 0.379/0.377
   b awrt 0.622/0.623
   c awrt 0.905/0.906
12 0.733 (0.732)

Exercise 2A

1 The selection of individual elements of a population. Advantages: low cost, results obtained faster than a census, represents whole population.
2 Every item is observed/measured, e.g. National census for forecasting school places. Census of a nursery school for numbers of carriers of a virus.
3 All the harnesses would be destroyed in testing them.
4 a Cheaper, quicker.
  b The sampling frame is a list of all the members in the population.
  c The larger the population, the longer the list, so the larger the sampling frame.
  d The variability of the population doesn't changed how many members are in it, the list remains the same size so the size of the sampling frame isn't affected.

5 a 01, 06, 64, 65, 94, 41 or 01, 18, 70, 97 99, 56: others are possible.
  b 079, 056, 110, 086, 143, 108 or 136, 097, 148, 069, 137, 123; others possible.
  c 010, 441, 172, 193, 249, 569 or 010, 184, 561, 547, 570, 278.

Exercise 2B

1 A census is where information is obtained from every member of the population. A sample is a sub-set of the population's information.
  a A simple random sample is a sample that is taken so that every member of the population has an equal chance of being included, all sub-groups of size n are equally likely to be chosen and sampling is taken without replacement. It can be difficult in a large population.
  b A stratified sample is where the population is divided into mutually exclusive groups and is where the proportion of the sample in each of these groups is the same as the proportion with which the group occurs in the population. It is good in easily stratified populations but you need to know the structure of the population. It is the most representative statistically.
  c Choosing at regular intervals from an ordered list; good for large populations and easy to use; bias in ordered list can be a problem.
  d A quota sample has the proportions as for a stratified sample (see part **b**), but the 'quota' in each group allows the interviewer to choose who to interview to fill the quota required in the group. This is faster and cheaper than stratified sampling but can introduce 'interviewer bias' in who is interviewed.
2 a Divides population into mutually exclusive groups, where the proportion in each group in the sample is the same as that in the population.
  b Year 1: 8, Year 2: 12 and Year 3: 16
3 a Systematic sampling would be easy to use.
  b The ordered list would need to be truly random. Note that if the structure of the sample of 2000 were known, it would be possible (and desirable) to take a stratified sample. With such a small sampling frame it would be possible to choose a simple random sample using random number tables, which would be truly random!
4 a Stratified − three strata.
  b Questionnaire to 10% of each strata.
  c Advantages: information on each strata, results should reflect those of the population.
Disadvantages: not suitable if sample size is large, strata may overlap if not already defined.

5 a i Cost, takes less time than a census.

    ii List of sampling units used to represent the population.

  b Many possible answers, e.g.

    i shoppers at a supermarket when considering shopping

    ii students in a secondary school when looking at school meals

    iii voters asked which party they are going to vote for.

6 $k = \frac{480}{30} = 16$

Randomly select a number between 1 and 16. Starting with the worker with this clock number select the workers that have every 16th clock number after this.

Mixed exercise 2C

1 a 12, 60, 73, 9, 41, 20, 04, 36

  b Say the population was a school year of size 76, each member of this population is written down in alphabetical order and numbered. Students whose numbers correspond to the numbers from the table are selected. Repeats are ignored.

2 a i Advantage: very accurate; disadvantage: expensive (time consuming).

    ii Advantage: easier data collection (quick, cheap); disadvantage: possible bias.

  b Assign unique 3-digit identifiers 000, 001, ..., 499 to each member of the population. Work along rows of random number tables generating 3-digit numbers. If these correspond to an identifier then include the corresponding member in the sample; ignore repeats and numbers greater than 499. Repeat this process until the sample contains 100 members.

3 a i Collection of individual items.

    ii List of sampling units.

  b i List of registered owners from DVLC.

    ii List of people visiting a doctor's clinic in Oxford in July 1996.

4 Assign unique 3-digit identifiers 000, 001, ..., 199 to the clients. Work along random tables rows generating 3-digit numbers – include the members corresponding to these numbers in the sample, ignoring repeats and numbers larger than 199. Repeat this until the sample includes 40 members.

5 a Advantage – the results are the most representative of the population since the structure of the sample reflects the structure of the population.

Disadvantage – you need to know the structure of the population before you can take a stratified sample.

  b Advantage – quick and cheap.

Disadvantage – can introduce bias (e.g. if the sample, by chance, only includes very tall people in an investigation into heights of students).

6 a People not in office not represented.

  b i Get a list of the 300 workers at the factory.

$\frac{300}{30} = 10$ so choose one of the first ten workers on the list at random and every subsequent 10th worker on the list,

e.g. if person 7 is chosen, then the sample includes workers 7, 17, 27, ..., 297.

    ii The population contains 100 office workers ($\frac{1}{3}$ of population) and 200 shop floor workers ($\frac{2}{3}$ of population).

The sample should contain $\frac{1}{3} \times 30 = 10$ office workers and $\frac{2}{3} \times 30 = 20$ shop floor workers. The 10 office workers in the sample should be a simple random sample of the 100 office workers. The 20 shop floor workers should be a simple random sample of the 200 shop floor workers.

    iii Decide the categories e.g. age, gender, office/non office and set a quota for each in proportion to their numbers in the population. Interview workers until quotas are full.

7 List separately men and women. take a simple sample of $\frac{65 \times 30}{150} = 13$ women and 17 men.

8 a Label members $1 \rightarrow 240$ Use random numbers to select first from 1–8 Select every 8th member (e.g. 6,14, 22, ...)

  b For example: more convenient, efficient, faster, simpler to carry out etc.

9 a i The group of all the individuals or items of interest in the investigation.

    ii A selection of individual members of the population.

  b Advantage: reduction in the amount of data to be analysed; disadvantage: loss of reliability and accuracy (relative to whole population).

10 Stratified – gives all groups an equal chance to give their views.

11 a Stratified sampling

  b Uses naturally occurring (strata) groupings. The results are more likely to represent the views of the population since the sample reflects its structure. e.g. variance of estimator of population mean is usually reduced, either individual strata estimates available.

12 a Allocate a number between 1 and 120 to each pupil. Use random number tables, computer or calculator to select 15 different numbers between 1 and 120 (or equivalent).

Pupils corresponding to these numbers become the sample.

  b Allocate numbers 1–64 to girls and 65–120 to boys. Idea of different sets for boys and girls

Select $\frac{64}{120} \times 15 = 8$ different random numbers between 1–64 for girls

Select 7 different random numbers between 65–120 for boys.

Include the corresponding boys and girls in the sample.

Exercise 3A

1 a Not a statistic since μ not known.

  b Is a statistic – no unknown parameters.

  c Not a statistic since μ, σ not known.

  d Is a statistic – no unknown parameters.

2 a 172

  b 83.1 (3 s.f.)

  c 175 (3 s.f.)

3 i a $N(10\mu, 10\sigma^2)$ **b** $N(\mu, \frac{13}{25}\sigma^2)$

  c $N(0, 10\sigma^2)$ **d** $N\left(\mu, \frac{\sigma^2}{10}\right)$

  e $N(0, 10\sigma^2)$ **f** $N(0, 10)$

  ii a, **b**, **d**, **e**, are statistics since they do not contain μ or σ the unknown population parameters.

4 a $\mu = E(x) = \frac{22}{5}$ or 4.4

$\sigma^2 = 11.04$ or $\frac{276}{25}$

b {1, 1} {1, 5}$^{\times 2}$ {1, 10}$^{\times 2}$

{5, 5} {5, 10}$^{\times 2}$

{10, 10}

c

$\bar{x}$	1	3	5	5.5	7.5	10
$P(\bar{X} = \bar{x})$	$\frac{4}{25}$	$\frac{8}{25}$	$\frac{4}{25}$	$\frac{4}{25}$	$\frac{4}{25}$	$\frac{1}{25}$

e.g. $P(\bar{X} = 5.5) = \frac{4}{25}$

d $E(\bar{X}) = 1 \times \frac{4}{25} + 3 \times \frac{8}{25} + \ldots + 10 \times \frac{1}{25} = 4.4 = \mu$

$Var(\bar{X}) = 1^2 \times \frac{4}{25} + 3^2 \times \frac{8}{25} + \ldots + 10^2 \times \frac{1}{25} - 4.4^2$

$= 5.52 = \frac{\sigma^2}{2}$

Exercise 3B

1 a $\bar{x} = 19.3, s^2 = 3.98$

b $\bar{x} = 3.375, s^2 = 4.65$

c $\bar{x} = 223, s^2 = 7174$

d $\bar{x} = 0.5833, s^2 = 0.0269$

2 a 29.2 (3 s.f.)

b 4

c 0.0225

d 2.24 (3 s.f.)

3 $\bar{x} = 236, s^2 = 7.58$

4 $\bar{x} = 205$ (3 s.f.), $s^2 = 9.22$ (3 s.f.), 9.22 (3 s.f.)

5 a $\mu = \frac{20}{3}, \sigma^2 = \frac{50}{9}$

b {5, 5, 5,}

{5, 5, 10}$^{\times 3}$ {5, 10, 10}$^{\times 3}$

{10, 10, 10}

c

$\bar{x}$	5	$\frac{20}{3}$	$\frac{25}{3}$	10
$P(\bar{X} = \bar{x})$	$\frac{8}{27}$	$\frac{12}{27}$	$\frac{6}{27}$	$\frac{1}{27}$

d $E(\bar{X}) = \frac{20}{3} = \mu, Var(\bar{X}) = \frac{50}{27} = \frac{\sigma^2}{3}$

e

m	5	10
$P(M = m)$	$\frac{20}{27}$	$\frac{7}{27}$

f $E(M) = 6.296\ldots$

$Var(M) = 4.80\ldots$

g Bias = 1.30 (3 s.f.)

6 a $10p$

c $\frac{X}{10}$ is an unbiased estimator of p.

7 a $E(X) = 0$

$\therefore \ E(X^2) = \frac{\alpha^2}{3}$

Exercise 3C

1 a $\bar{y} = 16.2, s_y^2 = 12.0$ (3 s.f.)

b $w = 15.92, s_w^2 = 10.34$

c $\frac{s_x}{\sqrt{20}} = 0.632$ (3 s.f.), $\frac{s_y}{\sqrt{20}} = 0.633$ (3 s.f.),

$\frac{s_w}{\sqrt{50}} = 0.455$ (3 s.f.)

d Prefer to use w since it is based on a larger sample size and has smallest standard error.

2 a $\bar{x} = 65, s_x^2 = 9.74$ (3 s.f.)

b need a sample of 37 or more

c 65.6 (3 s.f.)

3 need a sample of 28 (or more)

4 a 4.89

b 0.0924 (3 s.f.)

c need $n = 35$ (or more)

5 a $E(X_1) = np, E(X_2) = 2np, Var(X_1) = np\ (1 - p),$
$Var(X_2) = 2np\ (1 - p)$

b Prefer $\frac{X_2}{2n}$ since based on larger sample (and therefore will have smaller variance)

e $Var(Y)$ is smallest so Y is the best estimator.

f $\frac{p}{3}$

6 d $T = \frac{n}{m + n}\bar{X} + \frac{m}{m + n}\bar{Y}$ or $\frac{n\bar{X} + m\bar{Y}}{m + n}$

7 a $\mu = 1, \sigma^2 = 0.8$ or $\frac{4}{5}$

b {0, 0, 0} {0, 0, 1}$^{\times 3}$ {0, 0, 2}$^{\times 3}$
{1, 1, 1} {1, 1, 0}$^{\times 3}$ {1, 1, 2}$^{\times 3}$
{2, 2, 2} {2, 2, 0}$^{\times 3}$ {2, 2, 1}$^{\times 3}$ {0, 1, 2}$^{\times 3! = 6}$

c

$\bar{x}$	0	$\frac{1}{2}$	$\frac{2}{3}$	1	$\frac{4}{3}$	$\frac{5}{3}$	2
$P(\bar{X} = \bar{x})$	$\frac{8}{125}$	$\frac{12}{125}$	$\frac{30}{125}$	$\frac{25}{125}$	$\frac{30}{125}$	$\frac{12}{125}$	$\frac{8}{125}$

d $E(\bar{X}) = 1\ (= \mu)$

$Var(\bar{X}) = \frac{4}{15}\left(= \frac{\sigma^2}{3}\right)$

e

n	0	1	2
$P(N = n)$	$\frac{44}{125}$	$\frac{37}{125}$	$\frac{44}{125}$

f $E(N) = 1$

$Var(N) = 0 + 1^2 \times \frac{37}{125} + 2^2 \times \frac{44}{125} - 1^2 = \frac{88}{125}\ (= \sigma^2)$

h $Var(\bar{X}) < Var(N)$ choose $\bar{X}$

Exercise 3D

1 a 0.007

2 a 0.251 or 0.252

b 0.0098 ~ 0.0096

3 a 0.0668 or 0.066807

b $n = 241$ (or more)

4 a $\mu = 2, \sigma^2 = 0.5$

b awrt 0.186 ~ 0.187

5 a awrt 0.042

b awrt 0.013

6 awrt 0.11

7 awrt 0.061

8 a awrt 0.0019

b awrt 0.042

9 need n at least 1936

10 awrt 0.0197 ~ 0.198

11 a awrt 0.136 ~ 0.137

b 312

12 need 97 (accept 96)

Exercise 3E

1 a (124, 132)

b (123, 133)

2 a (83.7, 86.3)

b (83.4, 86.6)

3 (20.6, 25.4)

4 a $n = 609$

b $n = 865$

c $n = 1493$

5 a $n = 98$

b $n = 139$

c $n = 239$

6 (1.76, 2.04)

7 (304, 316) (3 s.f.)

8 (73 113, 78 631) (nearest integer)

or (73 100, 78 600) (3s.f.)

9 a Must assume that these students form a random sample or that they are representative of the population.

b (66.7, 70.1)

c If $\mu = 65.3$ that is outside the C.I. so the examiner's sample was not representative. The examiner marked more better than average candidates.

10 b (77.7, 79.7) (3 s.f.)

11 a (23.2, 26.8) is 95% C.I. since it is the narrower interval.

b 0.918

c 25

12 a (83.3, 87.3) (3 s.f.)

b (82.5, 88.1) (3 s.f.)

c (82.2, 88.4) (3 s.f.)

13 a (130, 140)

b 85%

c Need $n = 189$ or more

14 (30.4, 32.4) (3 s.f.)

15 (258, 274) (3 s.f.)

16 a 0.3108

b 0.8664

c (21.8, 23.3) (3 s.f.)

Exercise 3F

1 Not significant. Accept H_0.

2 Significant. Reject H_0.

3 Not significant. Accept H_0.

4 Significant. Reject H_0.

5 Not significant. Accept H_0.

6 $\overline{X} < 119.39...$ or 119 (3 s.f.)

7 $\overline{X} > 13.2$

8 $\overline{X} < 84.3$

9 $\overline{X} > 0.877$ or $\overline{X} < -0.877$

10 $\overline{X} > -7.31$ or $\overline{X} < -8.69$

11 Result is significant so reject H_0.

There is evidence that the new formula is an improvement.

12 Result is significant so reject H_0.

There is evidence to support the psychologist's theory.

13 $\sigma = 0.15$, $n = 30$, $\bar{x} = 8.95$

H_0: $\mu = 9$ (no change)

H_1: $\mu \neq 9$ (change in mean diameter)

$$Z = \frac{8.95 - 9}{0.15} = -1.8257 \text{ 5% C.I. is } Z = \pm 1.96$$

$-1.8357... > -1.96$ so result is not significant.

There is insufficient evidence of a change in mean diameter.

14 a $\bar{x} = 11.2$, $s^2 = 2.54$

b $1.976... > 1.6449$ so the result is significant.

There is evidence that the fish off the coast of Eastern Scotland are longer than those off the coast of Wales.

15 a Central Limit Theorem enables you to assume that $\overline{X}$ has a normal distribution no matter what the distribution of X since it states that no matter what the distribution of the parent population, provided the size of randomly chosen samples is sufficiently large, then the distribution of the mean of such samples will be approximately normally distributed.

b H_0: $\mu = 800$ (claim is true)

H_1: $\mu \neq 800$ (claim is false)

$$\text{t.s.} = Z = \frac{789 - 800}{\frac{42}{\sqrt{120}}} = -2.869... \quad \text{c.v.} = z = \pm 1.96$$

$-2.869 < -1.96$ so the result is significant.

There is evidence that the mean length of lifetime of the bulbs is not 800 hours. Suspect the claim made by the firm.

Exercise 3G

1 H_0: $\mu_1 = \mu_2$ H_1: $\mu_1 > \mu_2$ 5% c.v. is $z = 1.6449$

$$\text{t.s.} = Z = \frac{(23.8 - 21.5) - 0}{\sqrt{\frac{5^2}{15} + \frac{4.8^2}{20}}} = 1.3699...$$

$1.3699 < 1.6449$ so result is not significant, accept H_0.

2 H_0: $\mu_1 = \mu_2$ H_1: $\mu_1 \neq \mu_2$ 5% c.v. is $z = \pm 1.96$

$$\text{t.s.} = Z = \frac{(51.7 - 49.6) - 0}{\sqrt{\frac{4.2^2}{30} + \frac{3.6^2}{25}}}$$

[Choose $\bar{x}_2 - \bar{x}_1$ to get $z > 0$]

t.s. $Z = 1.996... > 1.96$ so result is significant. Reject H_0.

3 H_0: $\mu_1 = \mu_2$ H_1: $\mu_1 < \mu_2$ 1% c.v. is $z = -2.3263$

$$\text{t.s.} = Z = \frac{(3.62 - 4.11) - 0}{\sqrt{\frac{0.81^2}{25} + \frac{0.75^2}{36}}} = -2.3946...$$

t.s. $= -2.3946... < -2.3263$ so result is significant

Reject H_0.

4 H_0: $\mu_1 = \mu_2$ H_1: $\mu_1 \neq \mu_2$ 1% c.v. is $z = \pm 2.5758$

$$\text{t.s.} = Z = \frac{(112.0 - 108.1) - 0}{\sqrt{\frac{8.2^2}{85} + \frac{11.3^2}{100}}} = 2.712... > 2.5758$$

significant result so reject H_0.

Central Limit Theorem applies since n_1, n_2 are large and enables you to assume $\overline{X}_1$ and $\overline{X}_2$ are both normally distributed.

5 H_0: $\mu_1 = \mu_2$ H_1: $\mu_1 > \mu_2$ 5% c.v. is $z = 1.96$

$$\text{t.s.} = Z = \frac{(72.6 - 69.5) - 0}{\sqrt{\frac{18.3^2}{100} + \frac{15.4^2}{150}}} = 1.396... < 1.96$$

Result is not significant so accept H_0.

Central Limit Theorem applies since n_1, n_2 are both large and enables you to assume $\overline{X}_1$ and $\overline{X}_2$ are normally distributed.

6 H_0: $\mu_1 = \mu_2$ H_1: $\mu_1 < \mu_2$ 1% c.v. is $z = -2.3263$

$$\text{t.s.} = Z = \frac{(0.863 - 0.868) - 0}{\sqrt{\frac{0.013^2}{120} + \frac{0.015^2}{90}}}$$

$$= -2.5291... < -2.3263$$

Result is significant so reject H_0.

Central Limit Theorem is used to assume $\overline{X}_1$ and $\overline{X}_2$ are normally distributed since both samples are large.

7 Not significant. There is insufficient evidence to suggest that the machines are producing pipes of different lengths.

Exercise 3H

1 $2.34 > 1.6449$ so the result is significant.

There is evidence that Quickdry dries faster than Speedicover.

2 a Not significant. There is insufficient evidence to confirm that mean expenditure in the week is more than at weekends.

b We have assumed that $s_1 = \sigma_1$ and $s_2 = \sigma_2$.

3 a Not significant. Insufficient evidence to support a change in mean mass.

  b We have assumed that $s = \sigma$ since n is large.

4 a Not significant so accept H_0.

  b t.s. = 1.6535... > 1.6449
    Significant so reject H_0.

  c We have assumed that $s_A = \sigma_A$ and $s_B = \sigma_B$ since the samples are both large.

5 t.s. = −1.944... < −1.6449
    Significant. There is evidence that the weights of chocolate bars are less than the stated value.

6 a Result is significant. There is evidence of difference in mean age of first-time mothers between these two dates.

  b There is no need to have to assume that both populations were normally distributed since both samples were large so the Central Limit Theorem allows you to assume both sample means are normally distributed.
    We have assumed that $s_1 = \sigma_1$ and $s_2 = \sigma_2$.

Exercise 3I

1 a t.s. = 2.645 > 1.6449
    Result is significant so reject H_0.
    There is evidence that the new bands are better.

  b (46.7, 47.6) (3 s.f.)

2 a 0.185 (3 d.p.)

  b (4.10, 4.96) (3 s.f.)

  c 0.3520, accept awrt 0.352 ~ 0.353

3 0.04 (2 d.p.)

4 The smallest value of n is 14.

5 a (41.1, 47.3) (3 s.f.)

  b t.s. = −1.375 > −1.6449
    Not significant so accept H_0. There is insufficient evidence to support the headteachers' claim.

6 $\bar{X} > 7.66$ (3 s.f.)

7 t.s. = −1.5491... > −1.6449
    Not significant so accept H_0. There is insufficient evidence to suggest that the mean contents of a bottle is lower than the manufacturer's claim.

8 a $\bar{X} \sim N\left(\mu_1\,\dfrac{\sigma^2}{n}\right)$

  b need $n = 28$ or more

9 a 4.84

  b i assume that $\bar{X}$ has a normal distribution
    ii assume that the sample was random

  c (−0.346, 1.85) (3 s.f.)

  d Since 0 is in the interval it is reasonable to assume that trains do arrive on time.

10 a $\bar{X} \sim N\left(\mu_1\,\dfrac{\sigma^2}{n}\right)$

  b 95% C.I. is an interval within which we are 95% confident μ lies.

  c (3.37, 14.1) (3 s.f.)

  d (9.07, 10.35) (nearest penny)

  e t.s. = 1.8769... > 1.6449
    Significant so reject H_0. There is evidence that the mean sales of unleaded petrol in 1990 were greater than in 1989.

  f $n = 163$

11 a A 98% C.I. is an interval within which we are 98% sure the population mean will lie.

  b 0.182 (3 d.p.)

  c (9.84, 10.56) (2 d.p.)

  d need $n = 13$

12 a accept 0.109 or 0.110 (3 d.p.)

  b accept 0.002 (3 d.p.)

  c t.s. = −1.4766... < −1.2816
    Significant – reject H_0. There is evidence that his mean weekly driving distance has been reduced.

13 a accept 0.032 ~ 0.034

  b accept < 0.069

  c t.s. = 1.4815... < 1.6449
    Not significant so accept H_0. Insufficient evidence of an increase in the mean breaking strength of climbing rope.

14 b t.s. = 2.0165... < 2.3263
    Not significant so accept H_0. There is insufficient evidence of a deviation in mean from 1010. So we can assume condition **i** is being met.

15 a $E(X) = \mu$, $Var(\bar{X}) = \dfrac{\sigma^2}{n}$

  b i $\bar{X} \sim N\left(\mu,\dfrac{\sigma^2}{n}\right)$ **ii** $\bar{X} \sim N\left(\mu,\dfrac{\sigma^2}{n}\right)$

  c (17.7, 19.3) (3 s.f.)

  d $n = 278$ or more

  e t.s. = −2.1176... < −1.96
    Significant so reject H_0. There is evidence that the mean of till receipts in 1984 is different from the mean value in 1983.

16 a accept awrt 0.845 ~ 0.846

  b t.s. = 3.0145... > 2.5758
    Significant so reject H_0. There is evidence that the mean length of eggs from this island is different from elsewhere.

17 a accept awrt 0.413 ~ 0.414
    So out of 200 ≈ 83 samples will have mean < 0.823

  b (0.823, 0.845) (3 s.f.)

  c Since 0.82$\dot{4}$ is in the C.I. we can conclude that there is insufficient evidence of a malfunction.

Review Exercise 1

1 Significant *or* reject H_0 *or* in critical region.
    There is evidence that the (mean) time to complete the puzzles has reduced.

2 a 1.51...

  b 1.86 > 1.6449 so reject H_0.
    There is evidence that diet A is better than diet B or evidence that (mean) weight lost in first week using diet A is more than with B.

  c CLT enables you to assume that $\bar{A}$ and $\bar{B}$ are normally distributed.

  d Assumed $\sigma_A{}^2 = s_A{}^2$ and $\sigma_B{}^2 = s_B{}^2$

3 (127, 151)

4 a (0.542 to 0.544)

  b 0.16 or 0.4^2

  c 0.1217 (tables) or 0.1226... (calc)

5 a Advantages: Any one of
    • does not require the existence of:
      a sampling frame
      a population list
    • field work can be done quickly as representative sample can be achieved with a small sample size
    • costs kept to a minimum (cheaply)
    • administration relatively easy
    • non-response not an issue
    Disadvantages: Any one of
    • not possible to estimate sampling errors
    • interviewer choice and may not be able to judge easily/may lead to bias
    • non-response not recorded
    • non-random process

b Advantages: Any one of
- random process so possible to estimate sampling errors
- free from bias

Disadvantages: Any one of
- not suitable when sample size is large
- sampling frame required which may not exist or may be difficult to construct for a large population

6 a N(90, 0.25)

Application of Central Limit Theorem (as sample large)

b 0.0228

7 a 0.193

b (49.02, 50.98)

c (49.6, 50.4)

8 Need a random sample of $\frac{30}{600} \times 40 = 2$ from each of the 15 classes and a random sample of $\frac{150}{600} \times 40 = 10$ from sixth form;

Label the boys in each class from 1–15 and the girls from 1–15.

Use random numbers to select 1 girl and 1 boy from each class.

Label the boys in the sixth form from 1–75 and the girls from 1–75.

Use random numbers to select 5 different boys and 5 different girls from the sixth form.

9 a 30   **b** 4.84   **c** 0.5764

10 a 672.28   **b** (95, 126)   **c** 14.25

11 a 27.0   **b** (166, 170)

12 a 0.738 or 0.739   **b** 0.684 ~ 0.686

13 a Only cleaners – no managers i.e. not all types.

or Not a random sample 1st 50 may be in same shift/group/share same views.

b i Label employees (1–550) or obtain an ordered list

Select first using random numbers (from 1–11)

Then select every 11th person from the list

e.g. if person 8 is selected then the sample is 8, 19, 30, 41, ... 54

ii Label managers (1–55) and cleaners (1–495)

Use random numbers to select...

iii ...5 managers and 45 cleaners

c 390, 372 (They must be in this order.)

14 a Significant result or reject the null hypothesis.

There is evidence of a difference in the (mean) amount spent on junk food by male and female teenagers.

b CLT enables us to assume $\bar{F}$ and $\bar{M}$ are normally distributed.

15 a Population divides into mutually exclusive/distinct; groups/strata.

Its results will best reflect those of the population since the sample structure reflects that of the population.

b Advantages: Any one of
- enables fieldwork to be done quickly
- costs kept to a minimum
- administration is relatively easy

Disadvantages: Any one of
- non-random so not possible to estimate sampling errors
- subject to possible interviewer bias
- non-response not recorded

16 0.4875

17 a 7682.5

b Sample size ($\geqslant$) 97 required

18 a 0.9032

b 0.8810

19 a 0.1336

b 0.8413

c 0.1625 (or 016096 directly from calculator)

d All random variables are independent and normally distributed

Exercise 4A

1 H_0: There is no difference between the observed and expected distributions.

H_1: There is a difference between the observed and expected distributions.

2 11.070

3 a 11.070   **b** 20.090   **c** 15.987

4 18.307

5 13.362

6 20.090

7 11.070

8 a 5.226   **b** 21.026

Exercise 4B

1 a Expected value 20, $\chi^2_7(5\%) = 14.067$, $\chi^2 = 6.4$.

No reason to reject H_0.

b The values may be modelled by a discrete uniform distribution. A discrete uniform distribution is a good model.

2 a $\chi^2_4(5\%) = 9.488$, $\chi^2 = 4.49$

No reason to reject H_0. The binomial distribution could be a suitable model.

b Work out p calculated from the observed frequencies and use this to work out the probabilities.

(Note that this will reduce the value of v by 1.)

3 a H_0: the data may be modelled by Po(2).

$\chi^2_5(5\%) = 11.070$,

$\chi^2 = 4.10$

No reason to reject H_0.

b reduction by 1

4 Expected values 17, H_0: deliveries are uniformly distributed.

$\chi^2_5(5\%) = 11.070$, $\chi^2 = 5.765$

No reason to reject H_0,

5 a 1.4

b $\chi^2_2(10\%) = 4.605$, $\chi^2 = 5.04$

Reject H_0.

These data do not come from a Poisson distribution with $\lambda = 1.4$.

6 a 0.4

b $\chi^2_4(5\%) = 5.991$, $\chi^2 = 3.19$

No reason to reject H_0

7 Expected values: 21.6, 16.2, 27, 5.4, 10.8

$\chi^2_4(5\%) = 9.488$, $\chi^2 = 1.84$

No reason to reject H_0.

The number of accidents might well be constant at each factory.

8 $\lambda = 3.45$, $\chi^2_4(5\%) = 9.488$, $\chi^2 = 0.990$

No reason to reject H_0.

There is not sufficient evidence to suggest the data are not modelled by Po(3.45).

9 a Breakdowns are independent of each other, occur singly at random and at a constant rate.

b $\lambda = 0.95$, H_0 : the data can be modelled by Po(0.95)
Expected values; 38.67, 36.74, 17.45, 5.52, 7.14
$\chi^2_2(5\%) = 5.991$, $\chi^2 = 16.04$.
Reject H_0. The breakdowns are not modelled by Po(0.95).

10 H_0: prizes are uniformly distributed
H_1: prizes are not uniformly distributed
$\chi^2_9(5\%) = 16.919$, $\chi^2 = 10.74$
Do not reject H_0. There is no reason to believe the distribution of prizes is not uniform.

11 a $R = 43.75$ $\qquad S = 54.69$ $\qquad T = 43.75$
b $\chi^2 <$ c.v. so accept H_0.
Conclude no reason to doubt data are from B(8, 0.5).
c Mean would have to be calculated, an extra restriction.
c.v. would be $\chi^2_5 (5\%) = 11.070$.
$\chi^2 <$ c.v. so no change in conclusion.

12 a unbiased estimator of variance = 2.4
b It assumes goals are scored independently and at random, at a constant average rate.
c $s = 27.2$ $\qquad t = 78.4$
d H_0: the data are from Po(2.4)
H_1: the data aren't from Po(2.4)
e 3.5
f This expected frequency of $3.5 < 5$ so must be combined with $E(X = 6)$ to give class '6 or more goals' which now has expected frequency $7.2 + 3.5 = 10.7$
We now have 7 classes after pooling and 2 restrictions so degrees of freedom $= 7 - 2 = 5$
g $\chi^2 = 15.7$ $\qquad$ c.v. = 11.070
$\chi^2 >$ c.v. so reject H_0.
Conclude there is evidence that the data can not be modelled by Po(2.4).

13 b It is assumed that plants occur at a constant average rate and occur independently and at random in the meadow.
c $s = 37.24$ (2 d.p.) $\qquad t = 2.50$ (2 d.p.)
d $\chi^2 <$ c.v. so accept H_0.
Conclude there is no reason to doubt the data can be modelled by Po(2.59).

Exercise 4C

1 $\chi^2_2(5\%) = 5.991$, $\chi^2 = 0.899$
No reason to reject H_0.
No reason to believe N(3.8, 0.5^2) is not a suitable model.
2 $\chi^2_2(5\%) = 5.991$ $\chi^2 = 0.0381$
No reason to reject H_0. N(58, 4^2) might well be a suitable model.
3 $\chi^2_2(5\%) = 5.991$, $\chi^2 = 3.20$
No reason to reject H_0. No evidence to suggest N(8, 0.9^2) is not a suitable model.
4 a $\chi^2_2(1\%) = 9.210$, $\chi^2 = 4.79$, $\mu = 23.4$, $\sigma = 10.222$
Do not reject H_0.
The data could come from a N(23.4, 10.222^2) distribution.
b Shopkeeper could use this to help with stock control.
5 a $\chi^2_2(2\frac{1}{2}\%) = 12.833$, $\chi^2 = 44.4$ Reject H_0
b $\mu = 1.3165$, $\sigma = 0.0569$, $\chi^2_2(2\frac{1}{2}\%) = 12.833$
$\chi^2 = 5.78$ to 5.85 Accept H_0
c The outfitter should use the model in **b** because it is based on the experimental evidence.
S/he should order
size 1: 168 $\quad$ size 2: 417 $\quad$ size 3: 433 $\quad$ size 4: 182

6 b $t = 5.28$, $\quad r = 5.28$, $\quad s = 16.16$
c $\chi^2 <$ c.v. so accept H_0.
Conclude no reason to doubt the data could be from N(102, 6^2).

Exercise 4D

1 $\nu = 2$, $\chi^2_2(5\%) = 5.991$
2 H_0: Ownership is not related to locality
H_1: Ownership is related to locality
$\chi^2_2(5\%) = 5.991$, $\chi^2 = 13.1$
Reject H_0.
3 a $(3 - 1)(3 - 1) = 4$
b $\chi^2_2(5\%) = 9.488$.
Reject H_0. There is an association between groups and grades.
4 H_0: There is no relationship between results
$\chi^2_4(5\%) = 9.488$, $\chi^2 = 8.56$
Do not reject H_0. There is no reason to believe there is a relationship between results
5 $\chi^2_2(5\%) = 5.991$, $\chi^2 = 1.757$
Do not reject H_0. There is no evidence to suggest association between station and lateness.
6 $\chi^2_4(1\%) = 13.277$
Reject H_0. Gender and grade appear to be associated.

7 a Observed

	A	B	**Total**
OK	52	34	**86**
Def.	8	6	**14**
Total	**60**	**40**	**100**

Expected

	A	B
OK	51.6	34.4
Def.	8.4	5.6
	–	–

b H_0: Factory and quality are not associated.
H_1: Factory and quality are associated.
$\chi^2_1(0.05) = 3.841$,
$$\sum \frac{(O_i - E_i)^2}{E_i} = \frac{2^2}{45} + \frac{2^2}{28} + \frac{2^2}{13} + \frac{2^2}{25} = 0.6994$$
$0.6994 < 3.841$
Do not reject H_0. There is no evidence between factory involved and quality.

8 H_0: Gender and susceptibility to flu are not associated.
H_1: Gender and susceptibility to flu are associated.

Observed

	Boys	Girls	**Total**
Flu	15	8	**23**
No Flu	7	20	**27**
Total	**22**	**28**	**50**

Expected

	Boys	Girls
Flu	10.12	12.88
No Flu	11.88	15.12
	–	–

$\chi^2_1(5\%) = 5.991$,
Reject H_0. There is evidence for an association between gender and susceptibility to influenza.

9 $\chi^2_2(5\%) = 5.991$, $\chi^2 = 27.27$
Reject H_0. There is evidence of an association between the gender of an organism and the beach on which it is found.

10 $\chi^2_1(5\%) = 3.841$, $\chi^2 = 8.31$
Reject H_0. There is an association between age and the number of credit cards possessed.

Exercise 4E

1 23.209

2 15.507

3 $v = 8$, critical region $\chi^2 > 15.507$

4 $v = 6$, 12.592

5 H_0: Taking drug and catching a cold are independent (not associated)
   H_1: Taking drug and catching a cold are not independent (associated)
   $$\sum \frac{(O - E)^2}{E} = 2.53 \text{ (NB with Yates 2.09)}$$
   $v = 1$ $\chi_1^2 (5\%) = 3.841 > 2.53$
   No reason to believe that the chance of catching a cold is affected by taking the new drug

6 **a** H_0: Poisson distribution is a suitable model
       H_1: Poisson distribution is not a suitable model
       From these data $\lambda = \frac{52}{80} = 0.65$
       Expected frequencies 41.76, 27.15, $\dfrac{8.82, 2.27}{11.09}$
       $\alpha = 0.05$, $v = 3 - 1 - 1 = 1$; critical value = 3.841
       $$\sum \frac{(O - E)^2}{E} = 1.312$$
       Since 1.312 is not the critical region there is insufficient evidence to reject H_0 and we can conclude that the Poisson model is a suitable one.

7 27.5, 22.5; 27.5, 22.5
   $$\sum \frac{(O - E)^2}{E} = \frac{(23 - 27.5)^2}{27.5} + \dots \frac{(18 - 22.5)^2}{22.5} = 3.27$$
   $\alpha = 0.10 \Rightarrow \chi^2 > 2.705$
   $3.27 > 2.705$
   Since 3.27 is in the critical region there is evidence of association between gender and test result.

8 **a** Each box has an equal chance of being opened – we would expect each box to be opened 20 times.
   b $\chi^2_4 (5\%) = 9.488$, $\chi^2 = 2.3$
       No reason to reject H_0, A discrete uniform distribution could be a good model.

9 **a** 0.72
   b $\chi^2_2 (5\%) = 5.991$, $\chi^2 = 2.62$
       No reason to reject H_0. The B(5, 0.72) could be a good model.

10 $\lambda = 0.654$, $v = 2$, $\chi^2 = 21.506$,
    $\chi^2_2 (5\%) = 5.991$ Reject H_0.
    Po(0.654) distribution is not a suitable model.

11 $\chi^2_5 (5\%) = 11.070$, $\chi^2 = 2.36$
    No reason to reject H_0.
    The data could be modelled by a continuous uniform distribution.

12 $\chi^2_2 (5\%) = 5.991$ $\chi^2 = 4.74\dots$
    No reason to reject H_0.

13 **a** 4.28
    b $\chi^2_4 (5\%) = 9.488$, $\chi^2 = 1.18$
        No reason to reject H_0. Po(4.28) could be a good model.

14 $\chi^2_1 (5\%) = 3.841$ Reject H_0.
    There is evidence to suggest association between left-handedness and gender in this population.

Exercise 5A

1 **a** $\sum d^2 = 10$, $r_s = 0.714\dots$ limited evidence of positive correlation
   b $\sum d^2 = 18$, $r_s = 0.8909\dots$ evidence of positive correlation between the pairs of ranks

   c $\sum d^2 = 158$, $r_s = -0.8809\dots$ evidence of negative correlation between the pairs of ranks

2 **a** $\sum d^2 = 48$
   b $r_s = 0.832\dots$ The more goals a team scores the higher they are likely to be in the league table.

3 **a** $\sum d^2 = 68$
   b $r_s = 0.190\dots$ There is very little agreement between them.

4 $\sum d^2 = 20$, $r_s = 0.7619\dots$ The trainee vet is doing quite well. There is a fair degree of agreement between the trainee vet and the qualified vet. The trainee still has more to learn.

5 **a** The marks are discrete values within a very restricted scale.
       They are also judgements, not measurements.
   b $\sum d^2 = 28$, $r_s = 0.8303\dots$
       This shows a fairly strong positive correlation between the pairs of ranks of the marks awarded by the two judges so it appears they are judging the ice dances using similar criteria and with similar standards.

6 **a** Spearman's rank, because he is concerned with order.
   b $\sum d^2 = 100$, $r_s = 0.394$
       There is little correlation between the predicted and actual order,

7 $\sum d^2 = 30$
   $r_s = 0.464\dots$ There appears to be some positive agreement between the number of years a patient has smoked and lung damage but it is not very strong. It would appear that other factors need to be considered since the correlation is not very strong.

Exercise 5B

1 $H_0 : \rho = 0$; $H_1 : \rho \neq 0$
   a Critical values ± 0.3120. Reject H_0.
   b Critical values ± 0.3665. Do not reject H_0.

2 **a** $S_{xx} = 10.857\ 14$, $S_{yy} = 28$, $S_{xy} = -17$, $r = -0.975\dots$
   b Assume data are jointly normally distributed.
       Critical values ± 0.8745.
       Reject H_0: there is a correlation between x and y.

3 **a** $r = 0.677\dots$
   b Assume data are jointly normally distributed.
       $H_0: \rho = 0$;
       $H_1: \rho > 0$, 5% critical value is 0.5214. Reject H_0.
       There is evidence to suggest that the taller you are the older you are.

4 **a** The product-moment coefficient of correlation is the measure of the strength of the linear link between two variables. You could use it to investigate whether there is correlation between the age of a lichen and its diameter, for example.
   b **i** $S_{tp} = 255$ **ii** $r = 0.935$
   c $H_0: \rho = 0$; $H_1 : \rho > 0$;
       Critical value = 0.4973
       Reject H_0: there is reason to believe that students who do well in theoretical Biology are likely to do well in practical Biology.

5 **a** 0.686
   b critical value = ± 0.7067,
       Reject H_0. There is some evidence to show that the theory is correct.

6 $r = 0.793$, Critical value = 0.8822 Accept H_0. There is evidence to suggest the that company is incorrect to believe that profits increase with sales

Exercise 5C

1 $H_0; \rho_s = 0; H_1: \rho_s \neq 0$. Critical values ± 0.3610.
Reject H_0 : There is reason to believe that engine size and fuel consumption are related.

2 **a** $H_0: \rho = 0, H_1: \rho > 0$
$\alpha = 0.01$, critical value $= 0.7887$
Since 0.774 is not in the critical region there is insufficient evidence of positive correlation.

b $\sum d^2 = 46$
$r_s = 1 - \dfrac{6 \times 10}{8 \times 63} = 0.881$

c $H_0: \rho = 0, H_1: \rho > 0$
$\alpha = 0.01$; critical value: 0.8333
Since 0.8333 is in the critical region there is evidence of positive correlation.

d The data are discrete results in a limited range. They are judgements, not measurements. It is also unlikely that these scores will both be normally distributed.

3 **a** $\sum d^2 = 46$
$r_s = 1 - \dfrac{6 \times 46}{8 \times 63}$
$r_s = 0.452$

b $H_0; \rho_s = 0; H_1: \rho_s \neq 0$ critical values are ± 0.7381
(0.6429)
$0.452 < 0.7381$ or not significant or insufficient evidence to reject H_0.
No agreement between the two judges.

4 $\sum d^2 = 76, r_s = -0.357...$ $H_0: \rho_s = 0$;
$H_1 : \rho_s < 0$. Critical value – 0.8929. There is no reason to reject H_0.

5 **a** $\sum d^2 = 2, r_s = 0.943$
b $H_0 : \rho_s = 0; H_1: \rho > 0$. Critical value $= 0.8286$

6 **a** $\sum d^2 = 58, r_s = 0.797...$
b $H_0: \rho_s = 0; H_1: \rho \neq 0$. Critical values ± 0.5874.
Reject H_0: On this evidence it would seem that students who do well in Mathematics are likely to do well in Music.

7 **a** $\sum d^2 = 54, r_s = 0.6727...$
b $H_0: \rho_s = 0; H_1: \rho_s \neq 0$, Critical value 0.5636.
Reject H_0: the child shows some ability in this task.

8 $\sum d^2 = 64, r_s = -0.8285 = -0.829$ (3 d.p)
$H_0: \rho_s = 0; H_1: \rho_s \neq 0$. Critical value 0.8857.
Do not reject H_0:

Mixed exercise 5D

1 **a** $\sum d^2 = 58, r_s = 0.648...$
b The null hypothesis is only rejected in favour of the alternative hypothesis if by doing so the probability of being wrong is less than or equal to the significance level.

2 **a** Data given in rank/place order: a significance test is required and the populations are not jointly normal, etc.
b $\sum d^2 = 28, r_s = 0.766...$
$H_0: \rho = 0, H_1: \rho > 0, 2\frac{1}{2}\%$ critical value $= 0.06833$
Reject H_0. There is evidence of agreement between the tutors at the $2\frac{1}{2}\%$ significance level. At the 1% significance level the test statistic and critical value are very close so it is inconclusive at this level of significance.

3 **a** $\sum d^2 = 56, r_s = 0.66$
b $H_0: \rho_s = 0, H_1: \rho_s > 0$, critical value 0.5636
Reject H_0. There is a degree of agreement between the jumps.

4 **a** $\sum d^2 = 16, r_s = 0.714...$

b Critical value (5%) $= 0.7143$,
$H_0: \rho = 0, H_1: \rho > 0$
Reject H_0. At this level there is minimal reason to believe that the expert can date pottery. At the $2\frac{1}{2}\%$ significance level the critical value is 0.7857 which is bigger than the test statistic so H_0 would be accepted. At this level there is insufficient evidence for agreement.

5 **a** awrt 0.37
b Accept H_0. Critical value $= 0.3783$. No evidence of correlation.
c x and t bivariate normal.

6 **a** $\sum d^2 = 36, r_s = 0.5714...$
b $H_0: \rho = 0, H_1: \rho \neq 0$ c.v $= \pm 0.7381$
No reason to reject H_0. Students who do well in Geography do not necessarily do well in Statistics.

7 **a** 0.7857
b c.v $= \pm 0.7381$
Reject H_0. There is evidence to suggest correlation between life expectancy and literacy.
c Only interested in order; Cannot assume normality.

8 **a** $\sum d^2 = 24, r_s = -0.8285 = -0.829$ (3 d.p)
b Critical value $= 0.8286$
$H_0: \rho_s = 0, H_1: \rho_s > 0$.
Do not reject H_0. There appears to be no agreement between the ranks.

9 **a** $S_{xx} = 1038.1, S_{yy} = 340.4, S_{xy} = 202.2, r = 0.340...$
b one or both given in rank order
a significance test on r is required and population is not normal.
c $\sum d^2 = 112, r_s = 0.321$
d $H_0: \rho_s = 0, H_1: \rho_s \neq 0$, critical value $= \pm 0.6485$
Do not reject H_0

10 **a** $S_{xx} = 608.1, S_{yy} = 50\,288.1, S_{xy} = 17\,461.9,$
$r = 0.9368...$
b $\sum d^2 = 4, r_s = 0.976$
c $H_0: \rho_s = 0, H_1: \rho_s \neq 0$, critical value 0.6485
Reject H_0.

11 **a** $H_0: \rho = 0, H_1: \rho < 0$ c.v $= -0.5822$, reject H_0.
The greater the altitude the lower the temperature
b $H_0: \rho_s = 0$ (no association between hours of sunshine and temperature)
$H_1: \rho_s \neq 0$, critical value $= \pm 0.6833$
$0.767 > 0.06833$ so reject H_0. There is evidence of an association between hours of sunshine and temperature.

12 **a** You use a rank correlation coefficient if at least one of the sets of data isn't from a normal distribution, or if at least one of the sets of data is a letter grading or in order of preference. It is also used if there is a non-linear association between the variables.
b $\sum d^2 = 78, r_s = 0.527...$, critical value $= 0.5636$.
c Insufficient evidence of agreement.

13 **a** The null hypothesis is only rejected in favour of the alternative hypothesis if by doing so the probability of being wrong is less than or equal to the significance level.
b $\sum d^2 = 48, r_s = 0.4285...$
There is only a small degree of positive correlation between league position and home attendance.

14 **a** Critical value 0.5822, $0.972 > 0.5822$. Evidence to reject H_0. Age and weight are positively associated.
b $\sum d^2 = 26$ $r_s = 1 - \dfrac{6 \times 26}{9 \times 80} = 0.783$
c critical value 0.6000
$0.783 > 0.600$ is evidence that actual weight and the boy's guesses are associated.

Review Exercise 2

1 a $\frac{13}{21}$ or 0.619

  b $0.619 < 0.6429$ so accept H_0 or not significant.
So insufficient evidence of a positive correlation between judges
or
competitor's claim is justified.

2 a Reject H_0.
Conclude there is evidence of an association between Mathematics and English grades.

  b May have some expected frequencies <5 (and hence need to pool rows/columns).

3 a $p = 0.1$

  b $r = 28.5$ (1 d.p.), $s = 100 - 91 = 9.0$ (1 d.p.)

  c t.s. > c.v. so reject H_0.
(significant result) binomial distribution is not a suitable model

  d Defective items do not occur independently *or* not with constant probability.

4 a $r_s = -\frac{11}{15}$ or -0.733

  b Reject H_0, evidence there is a significant *negative* correlation between the price of an ice cream and the distance from a tourist attraction.
i.e. the further from a tourist attraction you travel the less you are likely to pay for an ice cream.

5 a $B(5, 0.5)$

  b Insufficient evidence to reject H_0.
$B(5, 0.5)$ is a suitable model.
No evidence that coins are biased.

6 $3.841 > 2.59$. There is insufficient evidence to reject H_0.
There is no association between a person's gender and their acceptance of the offer of a flu jab.

7 a $t = 0.12$

  b $3.25 < 11.070$. There is insufficient evidence to reject H_0.
Po(2) is a suitable model.

  c The mean must be calculated once then $\lambda = $ mean.
The expected values, and hence $\sum \frac{(O - E)^2}{E}$ would be different, and the degrees of freedom would be 1 less, also changing the critical value.

8 a The variables cannot be assumed to be normally distributed.

  b $r_s = \frac{5}{7}$ or 0.714

  c No evidence to reject H_0; No evidence of correlation between the cases of deaths from pneumoconiosis and lung cancer.

9 $14.18 > 9.219$ so significant result or reject null hypothesis.
There is evidence of an association between course taken and gender.

10 a

    i   ii

  b i $r_s = \frac{23}{28}$ or 0.821 (3 s.f.)

     ii $0.821 > 0.7143$ so significant result or reject null hypothesis.
There is evidence of a (positive) correlation between the ranks awarded by the judges or the judges agree.

11 a $p = 0.223$　　　b $t = 3.28$

  c H_0: $B(10, 0.2)$ is a suitable model for these data.
H_1: $B(10, 0.2)$ is *not* a suitable model for these data.

  d Since $t < 5$, the last two groups are combined and $v = 5 - 1 = 4$. Since there are then 5 cells and the parameter p is given.

  e $4.17 < 9.488$ so not significant or do not reject null hypothesis.
The binomial distribution with $p = 0.2$ is a suitable model for the number of cuttings that do not grow.

12 $3.47619 < 9.488$
There is no evidence of association between treatment and length of survival.

13 a

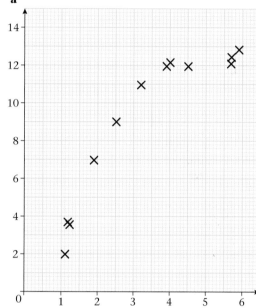

  b The strength of the linear link between two variables.

  c $S_{ss} = 26.589$; $S_{dd} = 152.444$; $S_{sd} = 59.524$

  d 0.93494...

  e $0.935 > 0.7155$
so reject H_0; levels of serum and disease are positively correlated.

  f Linear correlation significant but scatter diagram looks non-linear. The product-moment correlation coefficient should not be used here since the association/relationship is not linear.

14 Critical value $\chi_3^2(5\%) = 5.991$
from Poisson 5.47 is not in the critical region so accept H_0. Number of computer failures per day can be modelled by a Poisson distribution.

15 $2.4446 < 5.991$
so insufficient evidence to reject H_0.
No association between age and colour preference.

16 a $s = 9.28$

  b $12.12 < 15.086$ so accept H_0.
The distribution can be modelled by a $N \sim (360, 20)$.

Examination style paper

1 a Label children (1–32) or obtain an ordered list
Select first number using random numbers (from 1–4)
Then select every 4th person from the list

b Label children who come by car (1–12) and those that walk (13–32)
Use random numbers to select…
… 3 girls that travelled by car and 5 girls that walked.

2 a 0.6517
  b 0.9192

3 a 12.55333…
  b (100.3, 104.5)
  c 100 is not in the interval so reject the manufacturers claim.
  d The customers are not likely to complain since the machine is dispensing more than the stated volume.

4 a Since $2.782… > 2.5758$
    or $22.782 < -2.5758$
    then reject H_0 and accept H_1
    There is a difference in the lifetimes of the two different light bulbs.
    Alternative method using probabilities
    or $P(Z \geqslant 2.78) = 0.0026$ to 0.003,
    or $P(Z \leqslant 2.78) = 0.997$ to 0.9974
    or 0.0026 to $0.003 < 0.005$
    or 0.997 to $0.9974 > 0.495$
  b The Central Limit Theorem says that the mean lifetimes of both types of light bulb are normally distributed.

5 Critical value $\chi^2 = 5.991$, (critical value $\chi^2 < 5.991$)
  t.s. < c.v. Not in critical region. Accept H_0.
  no evidence of association between gender and the time spent watching TV.

6 b $r = 18.39$, $s = 0.37$
  c Critical value χ^2_2 (1%) = 9.210
    Since $12.88 > 9.210$
    it is significant, reject the null hypothesis
    The Poisson distribution is not a suitable model for the number of accidents per day on a stretch of motorway.

7 a $r_s = 0.539$
  b H_0: There is no association between mathematics and verbal reasonign scores.
    H_1: There is an association between mathematics and verbal reasonign scores.
    r_s 5% two-tail critical values are ± 0.6485
    $0.539 < 0.5636$ therefore accept the null hypothesis
    There is no evidence of an association between their mathematics and verbal reasoning scores
  c $H_0: \rho = 0$ $H_1: \rho > 0$
    r 5% one-tail critical value is 0.5494
    $0.583 > 0.5494$ therefore reject the null hypothesis
    There is evidence of a (positive) correlation between their mathematics and verbal reasoning scores
  d Spearman's rank does not use the actual data just the ranks.

Index